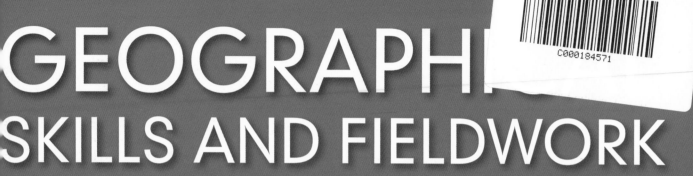

GEOGRAPHY
SKILLS AND FIELDWORK

for WJEC GCSE Geography and
WJEC Eduqas GCSE (9–1)
Geography A and B

Steph Warren

HODDER
EDUCATION
AN HACHETTE UK COMPANY

Orders: please contact Bookpoint Ltd, 130 Park Drive, Milton Park, Abingdon, Oxon OX14 4SE. Telephone: (44) 01235 827720. Fax: (44) 01235 400454. Email education@bookpoint. co.uk Lines are open from 9 a.m. to 5 p.m., Monday to Saturday, with a 24-hour message answering service. You can also order through our website: www.hoddereducation.co.uk

ISBN: 978 1 4718 6599 2

© Steph Warren 2017

First published in 2017 by

Hodder Education,

An Hachette UK Company

Carmelite House

50 Victoria Embankment

London EC4Y 0DZ

www.hoddereducation.co.uk

Impression number 10 9 8 7 6 5 4 3 2 1

2020 2019 2018 2017

Cover photos © age fotostock / Alamy; r © Aurora Photos / Alamy

Illustrations by Gray Publishing and David Gardner

Typeset in AvenirLTStd-Light, 10/12 pts. by Aptara Inc.

Printed in Italy

A catalogue record for this title is available from the British Library.

Contents

Acknowledgements

The publishers would like to thank the following for permission to reproduce copyright material:

Photo credits

p. 10 © Steph Warren; **p. 25** © Steph Warren; **p. 34** © GSO Images/The Image Bank/Getty Images; **p. 36** *t* © Steph Warren; *b* Skyscan.co.uk/© GeoPerspectives; **p. 37** *t* Courtesy of NASA-Johnson Space Center; *b* Skyscan.co.uk/© GetMapping plc; **p. 38** © Steph Warren; **p. 39** © Steph Warren; **p. 40** © Historic England Archive (Aerofilms Collection); **p. 42** *t* © Commission Air/Alamy Stock Photo; *b* © Steph Warren; **p. 43** © Steph Warren; **p. 73** *all* © Steph Warren; **p. 76** Courtesy of Peak Electronic Design Limited; **p. 78** *t* © Steph Warren *b* © GeographySouthWest/Moment/Getty Images; **p. 80** *all* © Steph Warren; **p. 81** *all* © Steph Warren; **p. 83** © Steph Warren; **p. 91** *br* © Steph Warren; **p. 92** *bl* © Steph Warren; **p. 94** © Steph Warren; **p. 97** © Steph Warren; **p. 98** © Steph Warren; **p. 102** *t* Skyscan.co.uk/© GeoPerspectives; *b* Skyscan.co.uk/© GeoPerspectives; **p. 105** © Steph Warren.

Maps on **pp. 1, 3, 91, 93, 95, 96, 99, 100, 103, 104** are reproduced from Ordnance Survey mapping with permission of the Controller of HMSO. © Crown copyright. All rights reserved. Licence number 100036470.

Numerical and statistical skills

In Chapter 1

Numerical and statistical skills you will:

→ study area, proportion, ratio, magnitude and frequency
→ work out the median, mean and mode of a set of data
→ work out the range and inter-quartile range of a set of data
→ calculate percentage increase and decrease for a set of data
→ describe relationships in bivariate data
→ interpolate and extrapolate trends in data
→ calculate Spearman's rank correlation coefficient.

↥ **Figure 15** A scatter graph of river width and river depth

Arithmetic mean

$$\bar{x} = \frac{\sum x}{n}$$

1 : 50 000

↥ **Note**: This map is not reproduced at original size.

1 Numerical and statistical skills

Exam Tip

Remember that scale is the relationship between the map and the ground.

Numerical skills

Some numerical skills are discussed in other chapters of this book such as scale in Chapter 2, designing fieldwork data sheets, collecting data with an understanding of accuracy, sample size and procedures, control groups and reliability and drawing informed conclusions from numerical data, all of which are dealt with in Chapter 4. Other numerical skills such as the quantitative relationship between units are dealt with in numerous places in the book. This section deals with the elements of numerical skills that have not been covered in other chapters.

Area

In geography, you could be asked about the area of part of a map or a photograph. An area is measured in square units. Therefore it is the length of an area times the width of an area.

For instance, if you want to know the area of a football pitch you will measure the length of the pitch and then the width of the pitch.

If the length of the football pitch is 100 m and the width of the football pitch is 50 m

100 x 50 = 5,000

So the area of the football pitch is 5,000 square metres (m²).

Working out the area of a feature on a map can be a little more difficult because of the irregular space it can cover. Also, you must remember to use the scale on the map to obtain the actual measurement on the ground.

Worked example

Look at the OS Wensleydale map extract on page 95. What is the area of the woodland in grid squares 8882, 8982, 8883, 8983 and 9083?

In order to achieve a measurement for this area, the woodland will have to be measured in two small sections as it is different widths and lengths. The measurements are an estimate of the size. See Figure 1.

Box shown on Figure 1	Map measurement cm	Ground measurement km	Totals km
1	2 cm x 1 cm	1 km x 0.5 km	0.5
2	3 cm x 1.5 cm	1.5 km x 0.75 km	1.12

Therefore, 0.5 + 1.12 = 1.62 sq km is the area of the woodland.

⬆ **Figure 1** How to measure woodland on a map extract 1:50 000

What is the area of Alnwick shown on the map extract on page 93?

REVIEW

By the end of this section you should be able to:

✔ show an understanding of area
✔ understand and correctly use proportion and ratio, magnitude and frequency.

Ratio, proportion, magnitude and frequency

A ratio is a comparison between two different things. In geography the most frequent ratio you will experience is the scale on maps, for example, 1:50 000. This means that for every 1 cm on the map there are 50,000 cm on the ground. You could come across questions about ratios on the examination paper.

Proportions can be built from ratios, for example a half is a proportion of 5:10. For example, half of the forest could be deciduous trees and half coniferous trees.

In geography, magnitude is the relative size of something. The term is used most frequently when assessing the impact of an earthquake. It is a measurement of the energy released by the earth. However, the term could also be used in relation to settlements. One settlement could have double the population numbers of another. One area could have triple the amount of average rainfall of another area.

Frequency is how often something occurs. Therefore, you could be asked about the frequency of volcanic eruptions or earthquakes in an area.

⊗ Learning objective

⊗ **Learning objective**

– To study statistical skills in geographical questions.

⊗ **Learning outcomes**

→ To be able to use appropriate measures of central tendency – median, mean, range, quartiles and inter-quartile range, mode and modal class.

→ To calculate percentage increase or decrease and understand the use of percentiles.

→ To describe relationships in bivariate data: sketch trend lines through scatter plots, draw estimated lines of best-fit, make predictions, interpolate and extrapolate trends.

→ To be able to identify weaknesses in selective statistical presentation of data.

Statistical skills

How to work out the median, mean and mode of a set of data

Median, mean and mode are known as measures of central tendency. They are useful ways to analyse any set of geographical data.

Median

This is the middle value of a set of data. The numbers should be arranged in rank order. If the number of values is odd, then the median value will be:

$$\frac{n+1}{2}$$

For example, if the total number of values in a data set was 39, an odd number, the median would be the 20th value in the rank order of the data.

If there are an even set of values, the median is the mean of the middle two values.

Arithmetic mean

The (arithmetic) mean is calculated by adding up all of the values in the data set and dividing the total by the number of values in the data set:

$$\bar{x} = \frac{\sum x}{n}$$

Where:

$\sum$ = the sum of

$\bar{x}$ = arithmetic mean

n = number of variables

Exam Tip

Rank order means in order of size from smallest to largest or largest to smallest.

Mode

The mode is the value that occurs most frequently in a set of data. If the set of data is very large, it may be a good idea to group the data into classes before working out the mode. The class with the highest frequency, with the most values in it, is the modal class. The modal class does not have to contain the mode of the set of data.

How to calculate the range of a set of data

The range is the difference between the highest and lowest value in the data set. For example, when looking at temperatures for a settlement for the year, the range of temperature would be the difference between the highest and lowest

temperature. Therefore, using the figures in the table for London below:

Highest temperature = 19°C

Lowest temperature = 4°C

Annual temperature range = 19°C – 4°C = 15°C

London average monthly temperatures:

Month	Jan	Feb	Mar	April	May	June	July	Aug	Sept	Oct	Nov	Dec
Temp °C	4	5	8	10	12	15	18	19	15	10	7	4

How to work out the inter-quartile range of a set of data

The inter-quartile range (IQR) shows the spread of a set of data, but is more accurate than using the range because it doesn't include the extremities. The IQR indicates the spread of the middle 50 per cent of the data set, as it omits the top and bottom 25 per cent. It gives a better idea of how the data is spread around the median value. This can also be referred to as percentiles with the 50th percentile being 50 per cent of the data set, the 25th percentile being 25 per cent and so on.

The IQR is calculated by putting the data into rank order highest to lowest or plotting it on a graph. The values are then divided into four equal groups or quartiles, where n is the number of values.

The upper-quartile (UQ) value is the value that occurs at the following position in the data set:

$$\frac{(n + 1)}{4}$$

The lower-quartile (LQ) value is the value that occurs at the following position in the data set:

$$\frac{3(n + 1)}{4}$$

The difference between these two values is known as the IQR.

Worked example

Consider the rainfall data for a city in Israel shown in Figure 2. This data could be either ranked or drawn as a graph to work out the IQR.

Year	Average rainfall (mm)	Rank
2008	200	9
2006	140	11
2004	452	2
2002	190	10
2000	290	6
1998	442	3
1996	347	5
1994	560	1
1992	390	4
1990	209	8
1988	235	7

Figure 2 Rainfall data for a city in Israel

To work out the IQR for the rainfall data:

$$UQ = 11 + 1 = \frac{12}{4} = 3$$

Third position = 200

$$LQ = 3 \times 12 = \frac{36}{4} = 9$$

Therefore the IQR is 242 mm.

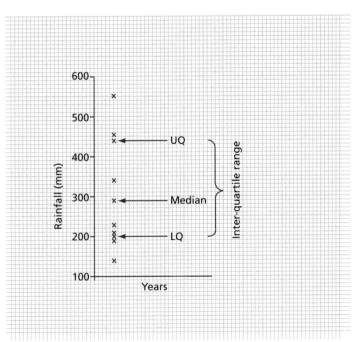

Figure 3 Dispersion graph of the rainfall data

ACTIVITIES

1 Work out the following measures of central tendency for the data in Figure 2.
   a Median
   b Mean

2 The results of a pebble survey along a beach in the south-east of England are shown in the table. The survey was completed using a quadrat. Ten pebbles were measured at each site.
   a Complete the table by working out the mean, mode and median for each site.

Sites	Distance along beach (m)	Size of pebbles (cm)	Mean pebble size (cm)	Mode pebble size (cm)	Median pebble size (cm)
1	0	8.5, 8, 7.5, 8, 6.5, 10.5, 4.5, 2, 7.5, 11			
2	50	8.5, 8, 7.5, 5, 6.5, 10.5, 4.5, 6, 7.5, 11			
3	100	6, 8, 7.5, 5, 6.5, 9.5, 4.5, 6, 6, 3			
4	150	8.5, 8, 7.5, 5, 6.5, 9.5, 4.5, 6.5, 6, 3			
5	200	8.5, 8, 7.5, 5, 6.5, 9.5, 4.5, 6, 6, 3			
6	250	4.5, 4, 7.5, 5, 6.5, 4.5, 4.5, 2.5, 3.5, 3			
7	300	4.5, 4, 3, 2, 3, 3.5, 5, 2.5, 3.5, 3			
8	350	4.5, 4, 2, 2, 8, 3.5, 2, 2.5, 3, 3.5			

   b Identify the advantages and disadvantages in each of these measures of central tendency.

How to calculate percentage increase or decrease in a set of data

There could be questions on the examination paper which ask you to calculate a percentage increase or decrease between two numbers. The way to work this out is to:

- work out the difference between the two numbers
- divide the increase (difference) by the first number
- multiply the answer by 100.

If your answer is a positive number, there has been a percentage increase between the numbers. If the answer is a negative number, then there has been a percentage decrease between the two numbers.

Worked example

For example, calculate the percentage increase in GDP for the UK.

In 2000 the UK had a GDP of US $1.5 billion. In 2014 it had a GDP of US$ 3 billion.

Therefore:

3 – 1.5 = 1.5 divided by 1.5 × 100 = 100%

The UK GDP between 2000 and 2014 had a percentage increase of 100%.

Country	GDP 2000 billions US$	GDP 2014 billions US$
Australia	0.4	1.4
China	1.2	10.3
India	0.4	2.0
USA	10.2	17.4
UK	1.5	3.0

Bivariate data

In Chapter 3, there is a section on scatter graphs (see page 64). There is information there on how to draw scatter graphs for bivariate data, how to sketch trend lines and lines of best-fit and how to describe the relationships that are shown on scatter graphs. However, you will also need to know how to interpolate and extrapolate trends.

- Interpolation is when a value is found inside the set of data.
- Extrapolation is when the value is found outside of the set of data.

ACTIVITIES

1 Study the graph on page 64 in Chapter 3. Interpolate the width for a depth of 65 cm. Extrapolate the value of the width for a depth of 110 cm.
2 Using the table on p. 6, calculate the percentage increase in GDP for Australia between 2000 and 2014.

REVIEW

By the end of this section you should be able to:

✔ use appropriate measures of central tendency – median, mean, range, quartiles and inter-quartile range, mode and modal class
✔ calculate percentage increase or decrease and understand the use of percentiles
✔ describe relationships in bivariate data: sketch trend lines through scatter plots, draw estimated lines of best-fit, make predictions, interpolate and extrapolate trends
✔ identify weaknesses in selective statistical presentation of data.

STRETCH AND CHALLENGE

Spearman's rank correlation coefficient

Spearman's rank correlation coefficient is a technique that is used to see whether there is a link between sets of data.

Here is a worked example to find out whether there is a correlation between settlement size and number of services in a settlement.

Step 1. The data should be put into a table, as shown, with the smallest number in the first set of data appearing first in column A, with its corresponding value in column C.

A	B	C	D	E	F
Settlement population	Rank	Number of services	Rank	Differences between ranks (d)	d^2
190	12	4	11	1	1
330	11	3	12	1	1
1,550	10	11	10	0	0
2,660	9	19	9	0	0
5,632	8	39	8	0	0
8,890	7	41	7	0	0
9,950	6	87	4	2	4
10,500	5	43	6	1	1
10,900	4	92	3	1	1
11,890	3	75	5	2	4
14,330	2	109	2	0	0
16,789	1	144	1	0	0

Step 5. The differences should then be totalled. In this example this is a result of 12. So $\Sigma d^2 = 12$. You will need this in the next part of the calculation.

Step 4. The difference between the rankings, column E, is then squared and added to column F.

Step 2. Both sets of data should be given a rank order, with the largest observation given 1, as is the case for 16,789. This settlement also has the largest number of services, so it also has a rank of 1. Ranking should be placed in columns B and D.

Step 3. Work out the difference between the ranks of each variable and add to column E.

Step 6. Calculate the coefficient (r_s) using the formula: $r_s = 1 - \left(\dfrac{6\Sigma d^2}{n^3 - n} \right)$

where Σ is the symbol for summation, d is the difference in rank of the values of each matched pair and n is the number of pairs.

Remember that $d^2 = 12$ from the above calculation and $n = 12$ (the number of pairs of data). Therefore:

$$1 - \left(\frac{6 \times 12}{12^3}\right) = 1 - \left(\frac{72}{1728 - 12}\right) = 1 - \left(\frac{72}{1716}\right) = 1 - 0.04 = 0.96$$

The result can be interpreted from the scale:

+1.0
Perfect
positive
correlation

0
No
correlation

−1.0
Perfect
negative
correlation

In the above example a result of +0.96 indicates that there is a strong positive correlation between settlement size and the number of services at these sites.

Further development of the technique

You should now determine whether the correlation has happened by chance or not. To do this you must decide on the rejection level (a). This is, if you like, how confident you want to be about your findings. Therefore, if you wish to be 95 per cent certain, your rejection level is calculated as follows:

$$a = \frac{100 - 95}{100} = 0.05$$

Calculate the formula for t:

$$t = r_s \sqrt{\left(\frac{n - 2}{1 - r_s^2}\right)}$$

Where r is Spearman's rank correlation coefficient (= 0.96), n is the number of pairs (= 12) and df is the degrees of freedom (this means how confident you are about your results). Therefore, with a rejection level of 0.05 or 95 per cent:

$$t = r_s \sqrt{\left(\frac{n - 2}{1 - r_s^2}\right)} + 0.96 \sqrt{\left(\frac{12 - 2}{1 - 0.96^2}\right)} = 10.73$$

(the critical value)

You should now work out the degrees of freedom:

$$df = n - 2$$

Where n = number of pairs = 12.

Therefore

$$df = (n - 2) = (12 - 2) = 10$$

Look this up in the t-table (Figure 4) using the degrees of freedom of 10 and a 0.05 rejection level. Therefore, the critical value is 10 and the t-value on the t-table is 2.23.

So the t-value is less than the critical value, which means there is a significant correlation between settlement size and the number of services found in them.

If the critical value is less than your t-value, then the correlation is significant at the level chosen. If the critical value is more than your t-value, then you cannot be certain that the correlation did not occur by chance. This could be because:

- your sample was too small to permit you to prove a correlation
- the relationship is not a good one to have chosen.

ACTIVITY

Work out whether there is a correlation between the distance from a groyne on a beach and the size of shingle on the beach.

Distance from groyne (m)	Size of shingle (cm)
50	7.6
100	7.9
160	8.2
300	6.8
420	7.4
480	6.8
550	5.8
670	7.9
850	6.8
950	4.7
1050	5.6
1150	4.2

Remember, if you have a joint rank (that is when two numbers in the table have the same value) you should add them together and then divide by the number there are, missing out the next numbers until you have omitted how many you add together.

Degrees of freedom	Rejection level probabilities				
	p = 0.1	p = 0.05	p = 0.02	p = 0.01	p = 0.001
1	6.31	12.71	31.82	63.66	636.62
2	2.92	4.30	6.97	9.93	31.60
3	2.35	3.18	4.54	5.84	12.94
4	2.13	2.78	3.75	4.60	8.61
5	2.02	2.57	3.37	4.03	6.86
6	1.94	2.45	3.14	3.71	5.96
7	1.90	2.37	3.00	3.50	5.41
8	1.86	2.31	2.90	3.36	5.04
9	1.83	2.26	2.82	3.25	4.78
10	1.81	2.23	2.76	3.17	4.59
11	1.80	2.20	2.75	3.11	4.44
12	1.78	2.18	2.68	3.06	4.32
13	1.77	2.16	2.65	3.01	4.22
14	1.76	2.15	2.62	2.98	4.14
15	1.75	2.13	2.60	2.95	4.07
16	1.75	2.12	2.58	2.92	4.02
17	1.74	2.11	2.57	2.90	3.97
18	1.73	2.10	2.55	2.88	3.92
19	1.73	2.09	2.54	2.86	3.88
20	1.73	2.09	2.53	2.85	3.85
21	1.72	2.08	2.52	2.83	3.82
22	1.72	2.07	2.51	2.82	3.79
23	1.71	2.07	2.50	2.81	3.77
24	1.71	2.06	2.49	2.80	3.75
25	1.71	2.06	2.49	2.79	3.73
26	1.71	2.06	2.48	2.78	3.71
27	1.70	2.05	2.47	2.77	3.69
28	1.70	2.05	2.47	2.76	3.67
29	1.70	2.05	2.46	2.76	3.66
30	1.70	2.04	2.46	2.75	3.65
40	1.68	2.02	2.42	2.70	3.65
60	1.67	2.00	2.00	2.66	3.46

Figure 4 A t-table

Cartographic skills

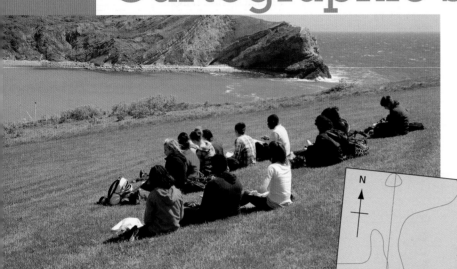

In Chapter 2

Cartographical skills you will:

- → extract, interpret, analyse and evaluate information from Atlas maps
- → extract, interpret, analyse and evaluate information from weather/synoptic charts
- → interpret and analyse topological maps
- → use and understand co-ordinates (grid references), direction, scale and distance
- → construct, annotate and interpret cross-sections and transects
- → extract, interpret and analyse information from maps (1:50 000 and 1:25 000 scales)
- → select and construct maps, using appropriate scales and annotations, to present information
- → use and understand gradient, contour and spot height
- → describe and interpret geo-spatial data presented in a GIS framework.

Height above sea level

- 2000+ m
- 400–2000 m
- 50–400 m
- 0–50 m
- 0 to –1000 m
- –1000 to –7000 m

N

Atlantic Ocean

IRELAND

UK

North Sea

English Channel

0   100 miles

0   100 km

Cartographic skills

⭐ Learning objective

– To study human and physical features on atlas maps.

⭐ Learning outcomes

→ To recognise and describe distributions and patterns of human features.

→ To recognise and describe distributions and patterns of physical features.

→ To be able to use latitude and longitude references accurately.

→ To be able to describe significant features of the physical and human landscape on atlas maps.

→ To analyse the inter-relationship between physical and human factors on atlas maps and establish associations between patterns on thematic maps.

Atlas maps

Atlases not only contain maps showing where places are, but also show physical patterns such as the height of the land and human patterns such as population density.

Physical features on atlas maps	Human features on atlas maps
Relief	Population distribution
Drainage	Population movements
	Transport networks
	Settlement layout

You will need to be able to describe these patterns and to understand how they relate to each other. Atlases contain maps at a variety of different scales, but the most common ones show patterns on a country, continent and world scale. You should be familiar with all of these.

How to describe the pattern of physical or human features on an atlas map

■ Begin with a general statement about where the features are located on the map. For example, in Figure1a China is densely populated on the eastern side of the country.

■ Then go into greater detail such as mentioning the area of the country, or any particular features such as the name of the sea next to that area, in this case the Yellow Sea.

■ You should then be more specific and include in the answer where the population is concentrated, such as the River Yangtze. In this section you could also give a reference using latitude and longitude lines.

Figure 1a Population density of China

Figure 1b Physical features of China

Figure 2 A relief map of the British Isles

Figure 3 Migration change 2004–2005 in the EU

Latitude and longitude

Figure 4 Tropical rainforests of the world

ACTIVITIES

1 Describe the distribution of tropical rainforests shown in Figure 4.

Answer the following questions:

➤ Where are most of the rainforests in relation to the named latitude lines?
➤ Which continent has the largest area of rainforest?
➤ Which continent does not have any rainforests?
➤ Name a country where rainforests can be found.

Use questions like these to help you to answer the following questions:

2 Describe the pattern of relief shown in Figure 2.
3 What would you add to Figure 2 to make the description easier to complete?
4 Describe the pattern of migration shown in Figure 3.

Latitude lines are the lines that go around the globe horizontally. The major lines of latitude are the Equator, Tropic of Cancer, Arctic Circle, Tropic of Capricorn and Antarctic Circle. These lines start at the Equator which is 0° and move north and south up to 90°N and 90°S respectively.

Longitude lines are lines that go vertically north and south on the globe. The major lines of longitude are the Greenwich Meridian and the International Date Line. These lines start at the Greenwich Meridian, which is 0°, and move east and west to the International Date Line, which is at 180°.

How to find a location using latitude and longitude

Latitude and longitude references are given in degrees and minutes from either the Equator or the Greenwich Meridian. The latitude reference is always given first followed by either N (north) or S (south). The longitude reference is then given followed by E (east) or W (west). A section of an atlas map for south-west England is shown in Figure 5. The reference for Tiverton would be 50°54'N 3°29'W.

⬆ **Figure 5** An atlas map of part of the south-west of England

ACTIVITIES

Using Figure 5:
1 Give the position of Exeter using latitude and longitude co-ordinates.
2 Which settlement can be found at co-ordinates 50°22'N 4°10'W?
3 Work in a pair. Make up four more questions for latitude and longitude. Your partner should answer them. Mark each other's work.

STRETCH AND CHALLENGE

Explain the relationship between the human and physical features shown on Figure 1.

REVIEW

By the end of this section you should be able to:

✓ recognise and describe distributions and patterns of human features on atlas maps at a variety of scales
✓ recognise and describe distributions and patterns of physical features on atlas maps at a variety of scales
✓ analyse the relationship between physical and human factors on atlas maps.

Exam Tip

When describing physical and human features, always start with the general and finish with the specific.

⭐ Learning objective

– to study weather and synoptic charts.

⭐ Learning outcomes

➡ To extract, interpret, analyse and evaluate information from weather/synoptic charts.

REVIEW

By the end of this section, you should be able to:

✔ extract, interpret, analyse and evaluate information from weather/synoptic charts.

STRETCH AND CHALLENGE

· · · · · · · · · · · · · · ·

Figure 6 shows a depression passing over the United Kingdom. Describe the weather associated with the passing of a depression.

Weather/synoptic charts

What is a weather/synoptic chart?

A weather (synoptic) chart is a map that shows the conditions of the atmosphere such as temperature, precipitation, wind speed and direction, atmospheric pressure and cloud coverage over a wide area for a specific time. The charts display weather conditions that have been recorded at many different weather stations across an area.

By studying the information, meteorologists can see how the conditions are changing and can predict what is likely to happen in the future. There are many different kinds of weather map but all are drawn using internationally agreed symbols.

ACTIVITIES

Study Figure 6.
1 What is the pressure at points A, B and C?
2 What are the weather conditions at London?
3 What are the weather conditions at Glasgow?
4 Explain the difference in the weather being experienced in Bath and Lowestoft.

Exam Tip

You will not be asked to construct weather/synoptic charts. However, you will be expected to have a good understanding of what they are portraying.

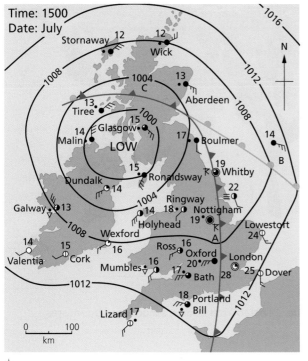

Present weather
= Mist
≡ Fog
, Drizzle
; Rain and drizzle
• Rain
✳ Snow
▽ Rain shower
⍔ Snow shower
⍔ Hail shower
⼉ Thunderstorm

Wind speed (knots)
◎ Calm
1–2
3–7
8–12
13–17

For each additional half-feather add 5 knot
48–52

Wind direction
Arrow showing direction wind is blowing from
i.e. ⟶ west

Cloud
○ Clear sky
◔ 1/8 covered
◔ 2/8 covered
◑ 3/8 covered
◑ 4/8 covered
◕ 5/8 covered
◕ 6/8 covered
◕ 7/8 covered
● 8/8 covered
⊗ Sky obscured

Temperature
Shown in degrees celsius i.e. 15°

Fronts
▬▬ Warm
▲▲▲ Cold
▬▲▬ Occluded

Weather station
Temperature—15 (Degrees Celsius)
Cloud cover
Present weather
Wind direction
Wind speed (Force)

Time: 1500
Date: July

Figure 6 Synoptic chart and weather symbols

Topological maps

What is a topological map?

There are two types of topological map. The first type includes maps of routes where the position of the place remains the same but the actual distance and direction are not so important. The other type of topological map shows the areas of a place but the size is determined by the value being portrayed.

- Maps of route networks. This is a map that has been made simpler. The actual distance and direction are not so important, but the position of places remains the same. If you were asked to give directions to somewhere, you would do it by perhaps drawing a map. The map would include the important features that you would pass on the route, such as large roads, railway lines and rivers. A good example is the London Underground map.

- Maps of areas such as countries where the size of the country has been changed. The size of the country is no longer its geographical size because it has been drawn to represent a different value. An example of this would be the number of migrants to a country.

Exam Tip

In the exam you would only be asked to complete a topological map. You may be asked why a topological map has been drawn to display that particular type of data.

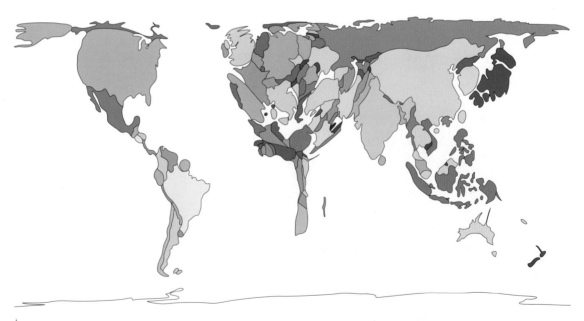

⬆ **Figure 7** A topological map of the amount of waste collected from homes, schools and businesses

How to draw a topological map of your route to school

- On a piece of paper, put the location of the house where you live and the location of your school. These should be in their correct situation in relation to the position of the places.
- Draw the roads that you would take from your house to school.
- Try to add some of the road names.
- Add on any railway lines and rivers that you would pass or cross on the route using different colours.
- Local services such as churches and public houses could also be marked.
- Add a key.

ACTIVITIES

1 Complete a topological map for your journey to school.
2 What are the advantages of topological maps?
3 Download and print a copy of the London Underground map (www.tfl.gov.uk/assets/ downloads/standard-tube-map.pdf) and outline how you would travel on the Underground between the following places. You should describe two different routes:
   a Waterloo station to Euston station
   b Victoria station to Liverpool Street station.
4 Using topological maps has a number of disadvantages. State two disadvantages of using the London Underground map.

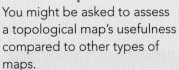

Exam Tip

You might be asked to assess a topological map's usefulness compared to other types of maps.

REVIEW

By the end of this section you should be able to:

- ✔ construct topological maps
- ✔ describe and explain the patterns that the topological maps show
- ✔ suggest appropriate uses of topological maps.

STRETCH AND CHALLENGE

• •

Study Figure 7, a topological map of the amount of waste collected from homes, schools and offices. Outline the main features of the map.

Ordnance Survey (OS) maps

Scale, symbols, grid references and direction

Exam Tip

Grid lines are always drawn so that they represent 1 km on the ground.

Scale

Maps are produced at different scales. The scale of the map is how much smaller the map is than the area it represents. On 1:50 000 scale maps, 1 cm on the map is 50 000 cm (500 metres) on the ground. On 1:25 000 scale maps, 1 cm on the map is 25 000 cm (250 metres) on the ground. The light blue lines which run horizontally and vertically across the map are called grid lines; they are drawn 2 cm apart on 1:50 000 maps and 4 cm apart on 1:25 000 maps. Every map has a scale line which can be used to measure distances.

Symbols

The symbols used on the map represent features on the ground. Many of the symbols give a 'clue' to what they represent. For example, a Post Office is the letter P. You will always be provided with a key but it is a good idea to familiarise yourself with OS maps so that you can interpret the symbols quickly without continual reference to the key.

An OS map symbols quick reference guide is provided below.

Feature	What to look for?
Woodland	Green areas with different types of trees identified
Water	Blue areas
Tourist information	These are symbols in blue
Fields	Usually white areas
Urban areas	Brown/beige shading
Roads	Motorways – blue A roads – green (major routes) and red (main roads) Secondary roads (B roads) – orangey/yellow Small side roads – yellow
Contours (showing height above sea level)	Thin brown lines. They are at 10 m intervals with every 50 m in a darker colour
Spot heights	These are a number next to a dot. They show the height of the land at the point where the dot is
Triangulation pillars	These are a number next to a symbol and also show the height at that point

Grid references

You will need to be able to locate features using four- and six-figure grid references. Four-figure grid references locate a square on the map and are usually used for large features such as an area of settlement or woodland. Six-figure grid references locate a particular point on the map such as a Post Office.

How to find a grid reference

Study the grid in Figure 8a. It has grid lines 2 cm apart and a number of symbols on it. To find the position of the Post Office in grid square 5885:

- Go along the bottom of the grid until you find the number 58.
- These are the first two numbers of the four-figure reference. The line will always be to the left of the symbol. Or if you were on the ground following the map, it would be the last grid line you walked over.
- Go up the side of the grid until you reach 85.
- These are the third and fourth numbers of the grid reference. The line will always be below the symbol you are locating. Or if you were on the ground following the map, it would be the last grid line you walked over.
- The symbol will be in the square right and above where these two lines meet.
- If you have been given a six-figure grid reference, the third and sixth numbers refer to the exact position of the symbol, for example 588857.
- You should complete the four-figure part of the reference to find the line and then divide the square into tenths in your mind, in this case, 8/10s as the reference is 588.
- Then complete the second part of the reference in the same way – 857.
- It is important to remember that for features such as a school, you will be given the word 'Sch' near a building. It is the centre of the building that is used for the six-figure grid reference.

8(b)

▲	Youth Hostel	♱	Place of worship with a tower
🚐	Bus or coach station	♦	Place of worship with a spire
△	Triangulation pillar	☐ Sch	School
⚑	Golf course or links	☐ Home Fm	Home Farm
P	Post Office		

8(a)

Figure 8 Four-and six-figure grid references

Exam Tip

Use four-figure grid references to locate an area on the map and six-figure grid references to locate a particular point.

Exam Tip

When asked which direction X is from Y, make sure that you start at Y and give the direction to X.

How to give a grid reference

Study the grid in Figure 8a. It has lines 2 cm apart and a number of symbols on it. To give the position of the youth hostel:

■ Give the number of the line immediately to the left of the symbol – it is 55.
■ Give the number of the line immediately below the youth hostel symbol – it is 84.
■ If a six-figure grid reference is required, you should divide the grid square in your mind into tenths as shown in Figure 8b. (This is double the size of the original square on the grid.) Each of the 1/10s is 2 mm because one grid square is 2 cm on the original grid.
■ Therefore the four-figure grid reference for the youth hostel is 5584.
■ The youth hostel is halfway across, 5/10s of the way or 555.
■ The line below is 84. Again split the grid square into tenths, going upwards this time.
■ The youth hostel is halfway up, 5/10s of the way or 845.
■ The six-figure grid reference is written 555845.

Compass directions

Map directions are given using the standard 16-point compass as shown in Figure 9. In an exam, when an OS map is used, north will be taken as being at the top of the map following the grid lines.

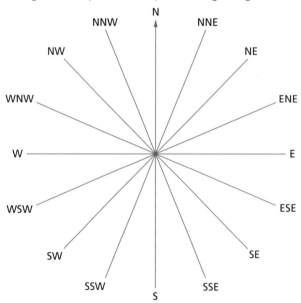

▲ **Figure 9** A 16-point compass

Exam Tip

Compass directions are often used with oblique photographs.

ACTIVITIES

1 Copy and complete the following table using the key for OS maps on the front and back covers of the book.

Symbol	Feature
TH	
☼	
	Tunnel
⋏ ⋏ ⋏	
	Non-coniferous Woodland
CH	

2 Copy and complete the table below using Figure 8a and 8b.

Symbol	Key	Four-figure reference	Six-figure reference
✝			
P			
△			
	Golf course or links		
□ Home Fm			
	Bus or coach station		
□ Sch			

Warkworth map extract (page 93)

3 Copy and complete the table below by drawing the symbol for flat rock found in grid square 2511.

Feature	Symbol
Flat rock	

4 Who owns the land in grid square 2408?
5 What type of woodland is found in 2007?
6 Identify three services in the village of Shilbottle in grid square 1908.
7 Complete the table by identifying five tourist features and their grid references found in Alnwick (north-west of the map extract). The first one has been done for you.

Tourist feature	Grid reference
Information	187133

8 Which direction is Alnwick from Alnmouth?
9 Which direction is Warkworth from Alnmouth?
10 Which direction is Shilbottle from Lesbury?

Exam Tip

Grid references and directions are often used relating to the location of photographs or features on a map.

STRETCH AND CHALLENGE

1 Study Figure 28. The photograph was taken at grid reference 267048. In which direction was the camera pointing?
2 Look at Figure 27. Which direction was the camera pointing when the aerial photograph was taken?

REVIEW

By the end of this section you should be able to:

✔ understand what is meant by the scale of a map
✔ recognise symbols
✔ use four- and six-figure grid references accurately
✔ demonstrate an understanding of direction using the 16-point compass.

Straight line and winding distances

Measuring straight line distances

When measuring straight line distances, it is useful to remember that on maps the grid lines are always drawn so that they represent 1 km on the ground. This can make measuring straight line distances very easy.

How to measure a straight line distance between two points such as two railway stations

- Use a ruler or the edge of a piece of paper.
- Mark on the piece of paper the location of the two points or take the measurement between the points with the ruler.
- Measure this distance against the scale line on the map or calculate the distance using the scale of 2 cm = 1 km.

For example, on the OS map of Swanage on page 104, the straight distance from the station at Corfe Castle to the station at Swanage is 14.6 cm or 7.3 km.

Measuring curved (winding) distances

Measuring the distance along a curved or winding route such as a road is more complicated. This can be done either by using a piece of string or by splitting the route into straight sections. The easiest way of measuring the distances along a winding route is with a piece of string.

How to measure a route (winding distance such as a railway line, road or river) using a piece of string

- The end of the piece of string should be placed at the beginning of the route.
- The string should be laid along the route following the curves as accurately as possible.
- The end of the route should be marked on the piece of string.
- The length of the string which equals the route can then be measured against the scale on the map or a calculation can be done on the basis that 2 cm = 1 km.

How to measure a route (winding distance such as a railway line, road or river) using straight sections

- The route to be measured should be split into a number of straight sections.
- The point chosen for the end of one straight section and the beginning of another is usually where the route bends.
- All of the straight sections can then be measured and the total distance converted into kilometres using the scale.
- The more straight sections that the route is broken down into, the more accurate will be the final measurement.

For example, Figure 10 is a section of the railway line on the OS map of Swanage on page 104. Notice how the line has been broken into straight sections.

Figure 10 Measuring distance on an OS map

ACTIVITIES

Wensleydale map extract (page 95)

1 Calculate the length of the River Ure from the bridge at Hawes (8790) to the bridge at Bainbridge (9390).
2 What is the approximate length of the A road between 875898 and 934904?
3 Which is the longest route?
4 What is the difference in kilometres?
5 How far is it from one of the sources of Bardale Beck at 865838 to its confluence with Raydale Beck at 911861?

Swanage map extract (page 104)

6 What is the length of the B3069 between its two junctions (9681 and 0078) with the A351?
7 Which is the furthest distance, travelling between these two points on the A351 road or the B3069 road?
8 How much further is it?

New Forest (Bournemouth and Poole) map extract (page 96)

9 What is the length of the railway line on the map extract?
10 What is the length of the River Stour between grid reference 133940 and 150922?

Exam Tip

To make measuring distances easier, always have a piece of string in your pencil case.

REVIEW

By the end of this section you should be able to:

✔ measure straight line distances on a map
✔ measure curved distances on a map.

STRETCH AND CHALLENGE

There are three ways to get from Corfe Castle to Swanage; two by road (either the A351 or the B3351) and one by railway. Which is the shortest route?

Suggest two reasons for taking the longest route to do the journey.

⭐ Learning objective

– To study cross-sections and transects.

⭐ Learning outcomes

➜ To be able to construct, interpret and annotate cross-sections and transects of physical and human landscapes.

➜ To use and understand gradient, contour and spot height.

How to construct a cross-section along the line X–Y in Figure 9

- Place the edge of a piece of paper along the line X–Y in diagram A.
- Mark the heights of the contour lines where the paper crosses them. This is usually done by putting a small line on the piece of paper and noting down the height at that point. Also mark the spot height which shows the top of the hill.
- Remove the piece of paper with the location of the contour lines and the heights marked on it. Place it on a piece of graph paper. Work out an appropriate scale for the y-axis and draw it on the graph paper. Mark points on the graph at the correct height and at the correct location as shown on diagram B. Point A, for example, is marked at 200 metres.
- You may draw lines up to the points as shown on diagrams B and C but it is perfectly correct to just draw the crosses at the correct point.
- Join up the crosses to show the shape of the land. In this case it is a hill with a steep slope and a less steep slope.

Cross-sections and transects

Constructing cross-sections

A cross-section shows the variations in relief along a chosen line. It is a graph which shows distance along the x-axis (horizontal) and height on the y-axis (vertical). When drawing a cross-section, the scale used on both axes must be chosen carefully to show a true representation of the area.

Diagram A

Diagram B

Diagram C

⬆ **Figure 11** Constructing a cross-section

Interpreting cross-sections

Cross-sections show the shape of the land. If the land is steep, the contours will be close together on the map and the line on the graph paper will increase quickly. If the land slopes gradually, the contours will be further apart and the line on the graph paper will increase more slowly. This can be seen in Figure 9. The first slope to the left of diagram A has a steep gradient with the contours on diagram A being quite close together. The contours to the right of diagram A are far apart depicting a gentle gradient that is reflected in the line of the graph on diagrams B and C.

Annotating cross-sections

Cross-sections show many physical features. As stated above, the most important feature is the shape of the land. Other physical features such as rivers can also be marked. Human features such as settlements and roads can also be located on a cross-section with explanatory points being made.

Transects

A transect is a line through a defined area along which characteristics are counted at regular intervals. It can be used to measure both human and physical features. Transects are often carried out along roads leading from the centre of a settlement. The age and use of buildings are noted every 100 metres. This shows how the land use changes in different directions from the centre of the settlement. Transects can be used to show changes in vegetation, for example on sand dunes. The vegetation cover is checked using a quadrat to assess the different type and species moving away from the sea in a straight line inland.

Exam Tip

In the exam, you could be asked to interpret cross-sections. However, it is important that you also know how they are constructed and annotated to help your interpretation.

Exam Tip

Make sure that you know what the following terms mean:

Gradient – the slope of the land.

Contours – the lines on a map that show height.

Spot height – the height of the land at a particular point on the map.

You could be asked to define them or just asked questions about maps that include these terms.

ACTIVITIES

Wensleydale map extract (page 95)

1. a Draw a cross-section from the 560 m contour line at Green Side (865851) to the 490 m contour line at New Close (884844).
    b Label the two rivers.
    c Mark on the cross-section where you think the photograph shown in Figure 12 was taken.
    d In which direction do you think the photograph was taken?
    e Justify your answer with reference to the photograph and the map.

⬆ **Figure 12**

2. a Draw a cross-section from spot height 511 m in grid square 8987 to spot height 379 m in grid square 9487.
    b Label four secondary roads less than 4 m wide, three streams, Semer Water and two areas of woodland.

STRETCH AND CHALLENGE

· · · · · · · · · · · · · · ·

Using the Wensleydale map extract on page 95, draw a cross-section from spot height 614 m in grid square 8786 to spot height 535 m in grid square 8892. Label the River Ure and the A684.

REVIEW

By the end of this section you should be able to:

✔ construct, interpret and annotate cross-sections and transects
✔ use and understand gradient, contour and spot height.

Physical and human features on OS maps

There are a number of physical and human features which you could be asked to recognise on OS maps, and you could be asked to describe the patterns they produce. It is important that you understand what the question expects you to write about.

The physical features that you could be asked about are:

Relief – the shape of the land. This can be seen by looking at the distance between the contours and the pattern that the contours show on the map. The height difference between each contour line (the vertical interval) is 10 m on 1:50000 maps. Every 50 m, the contour line is a slightly darker brown and has the height marked on it as shown in Figure 13 on page 27. On 1:25000 maps the vertical interval is 5 m with a darker contour line every 25 m. When writing about the relief, you should use actual figures from the map, as well as terms such as highland, lowland or steep slopes. These are meaningless without the actual height or the rate at which the height is increasing or decreasing.

Fluvial landscapes (rivers and their valleys) – the skills you require are to be able to:

- recognise the presence or absence of rivers or lakes in an area
- recognise the patterns that rivers make in an area
- recognise the direction that a river is flowing
- see the influence of human activity on rivers and their valleys
- describe a river and its valley
- compare river valleys on a map extract
- compare river valleys on maps of differing scales.

Coastal landscapes – the skills you require are to be able to:

- recognise coastal features such as cliffs and stacks
- see the influence of human activity on coastal landscapes
- describe coastal landscapes
- compare coastlines on a map extract
- compare coastal landscapes on maps of differing scales.

Vegetation – you will need to be able to recognise the type of vegetation, for example woodlands, orchards and parks, and describe their distribution on a map. These can be seen in the land features section of the key.

The human features that you could be asked about are:

Land use – this would include urban areas and settlement patterns in rural areas. Typical questions would ask about the settlement distribution of an area and the human or physical factors which might have influenced the pattern.

Communications – this would include routes such as roads and railway lines. You might be asked to comment on the pattern shown by the communication links or explain how relief has influenced the pattern.

⭐ **Learning objective**

– To study physical and human features on OS maps.

⭐ **Learning outcomes**

→ To extract, interpret, analyse and evaluate information about the physical and human landscape on OS maps.

How to describe the pattern or distribution of settlement on a map

- Begin with a general statement about where settlement is located on the map, such as 'in the south-east'.
- Then go into greater detail, such as 'the settlement is along the lines of communication and at the bottom of a steep slope'. This mentions both a physical and human feature, although this is not essential.
- You should then be more specific and include in the answer the name of the road and the height of the land.

For example, there follows a description of the settlement pattern on the Wensleydale OS map (page 95). The majority of the settlement can be found in a band across the centre of the map extract. The settlements are close to the River Ure. The largest settlement is Hawes in grid square 8789. The settlements are mainly found on the south side of the valley, an exception being Askrigg in grid square 9491.

Contour patterns	Commentary
uniform slope diagram, labelled 50	This is a uniform slope. The contours decrease evenly. The distance between the contour lines is the same all the way down the slope.
convex slope diagram, labelled 100 and 50	This is a convex slope. The contour lines are closer together at the bottom of the slope. This means that the height is increasing quickly because the slope is steep. The lines gradually become further apart towards the top of the slope. This means that the height is increasing more slowly and that the slope is more gentle.
concave slope diagram, labelled 50	This is a concave slope. The contour lines are further apart at the bottom of the slope. This means that the height is increasing slowly and that the slope is gentle. The lines gradually become closer together towards the top of the slope. This means that the height is increasing more quickly and that the slope is steeper.
V-shaped valley diagram, labelled 100	This is a V-shaped valley. The distance between the contours is regular, meaning that the valley sides will have an even slope. There is no flat land by the side of the river. This is shown by the presence of contour lines right next to the river. The V of the contour always points upstream. In this instance, the river is flowing from the top to the bottom of the page.
U-shaped valley diagram, labelled 50 and 50	This is a U-shaped valley. The distance between the contours is regular, meaning that valley sides will have an even slope. The contours increase quickly, meaning that the sides of the valley are steep. There is an area of flat land by the side of the river shown by the lack of contour lines. The contour lines do not cross the river for many kilometres; it is therefore very difficult to ascertain the direction of flow. On an OS map, other clues would be the presence of tributaries and the river becoming wider as it moves downstream.

Exam Tip

Remember that contour lines never touch or cross.

- The V of the contours across a river always points upstream.
- Contour lines which are close together mean steep slopes.
- Contour lines which are far apart mean gentle slopes.

◀ **Figure 13** Basic contour patterns of slopes and valleys

ACTIVITIES

Looe map extract (page 99)

1 Describe the distribution of woodland.
2 Describe the distribution of communication links in the area.

Swanage map extract (page 104)

3 Describe the distribution of settlement.
4 Woodland is being managed in the area of the map north of grid line 82. How does the map show that the woodland is being managed?
5 How have communication links been affected by the relief of the area?
6 Study the two map extracts for Swanage (pages 103 and 104).
   a Which is the largest scale map? Comment on your answer. Ensure that you include how the maps differ in the detail that they show.
   b Complete the table to show features that are only shown on that scale of the map.

1:50 000	1:25 000

c Which scale of map would be the best to use on a geography field trip?
d State two different ways in which each map can be used.

New Forest (Bournemouth and Christchurch) map extract (page 96)

7 What is the coastal landform found in grid square 1891?
8 Describe the coastal landscape found in grid square 1790.
9 Compare the coastal landscape found in grid square 1690 with that in 1491.
10 What is the fluvial feature found in grid square 1492?
11 Describe the fluvial landscape in grid square 1492.

Exam Tip

Settlement patterns sometimes form particular shapes. It is a good idea to use geographical terminology to describe these shapes, such as:

Dispersed – this is when the settlements/houses are spread out over an area.

Nucleated – this is when settlements are close together in an area.

Linear – this is when houses in a settlement are either side of a main road.

STRETCH AND CHALLENGE

Explain the communication links shown on the Cambridge OS map extract on page 100.

REVIEW

By the end of this section you should be able to:

✓ identify and describe basic landscape features
✓ identify major relief features on maps
✓ recognise and describe the patterns made by physical features such as relief (slopes), drainage (rivers and their valleys) and different types of vegetation
✓ describe the physical features as they are shown on large-scale maps of the following landscapes – coastlines, fluvial and glacial landscapes
✓ recognise and describe the distribution and patterns made by human features such as land use (settlement patterns) and communications
✓ compare maps.

Geo-spatial data

The people indicate where newspapers are delivered to each day.

This layer shows houses. The central building is a newsagent.

This layer shows the roads of the area.

Base map showing physical features.

Figure 16 A GIS map has a number of layers that can be placed on each other to build a picture of an area

What is geo-spatial data?

The word geo-spatial is used to show that the data being used has a geographic element to it. This means that it has some kind of location information such as co-ordinates. GIS is a form of geo-spatial data. Other geo-spatial data is GPS, which is used by thousands of car drivers and hill walkers, and satellite imagery.

What is GIS?

GIS is a system where geographic data is stored in layers and used in software programmes so that spatial information can be created, stored, interpreted and mapped. It allows a large amount of information to be seen by layering one set of information onto another.

Exam Tip

GIS could be used in many ways for the examination. You could be given information in the form of a GIS map and asked to extract information from it. You may be asked to analyse and evaluate information on GIS maps.

The advantages and disadvantages of GIS

Advantages	Disadvantages
A lot of information can be seen on one map.	The information can become difficult to see if too much is put onto one map.
Information can be linked together easily to form patterns that can be analysed.	A computer or other ICT equipment is needed as the maps are digital.
GIS is available on smartphones and tablets	The equipment is expensive to buy and keep up to date.
It is of great benefit to many public services such as the police and utilities.	A certain amount of training is needed to use the more sophisticated systems.
GPS has made travelling between places much easier.	

ACTIVITIES

1. What do the letters GIS stand for?
2. What is meant by the term 'layering'?
3. State four organisations or people who use GIS.
4. You order a pizza from a pizza delivery company. How could GIS be used to deliver your pizza?
5. A large supermarket chain wants to locate a new store in an area. The following layers were used to work out the best place for the store.
   a Population density
   b Land for sale
   c Transport routes
   d Competitors
   e Socio-economic groupings of residents
   Put the layers into the order that you think they would have been used. Justify your order.

⭐ Learning objective

– To study map evidence of human activity including tourism.

⭐ Learning outcomes

➡ To be able to interpret map evidence of human activity.
➡ To be able to interpret map evidence of tourism.

Human activity from map evidence

Maps show a large amount of human activity, the extent of which is shown by looking at the key. Communication routes such as roads and railways with their associated features such as tunnels and level crossings (LC) are shown. Other public rights of way such as footpaths and cycle networks are also shown on maps.

The section on the OS map key called 'Land features' contains a lot of information about the location of other human activity, for example windmills and wind generators. It also indicates who owns some of the land on the map, such as the National Trust.

Maps show settlements but not the number of people who live in them, although their actual size is shown by the area they cover. Some human activity is shown by the services available in settlements, such as churches, Post Offices and public houses.

Tourist information has its own section in the key on OS maps and many symbols are used to depict the variety of tourist information that is available on maps. As well as the information in the key, it is also important to remember that castles (in the antiquities part of the key) are also tourist attractions.

ACTIVITIES

Looe map extract (page 99)

1   Duloe has five services. State what the services are by drawing the appropriate symbol.
2   Figure 14 on page 31 is a sketch map of part of the Looe map extract. Copy and complete the sketch map with the following features:
    a   the West Looe River
    b   the settlement of Looe
    c   the route of the A387
    d   100 m contour line
3   Copy and complete the table using the sketch map and the OS map extract of Looe to help you.

Place	Feature on map
Island A	
Spot height B	
Tourist attraction C	
Tourist attraction D	
Road number E	
Road number F	
Settlement G	
Type of woodland H	
Farm I	

0   1 km   2 km

B roads

50 metre contour line

East Looe River

Railway line and station

Figure 14 An incomplete sketch map of part of the Looe extract

Exam Tip

Human activity may be examined by using a sketch map. On exam papers, it is better to shade rather than use different colours on sketch maps.

STRETCH AND CHALLENGE

• • • • • • • • • • • • • • •

Explain the presence of so many tourist information features on the Looe map extract on page 99.

REVIEW

By the end of this section you should be able to:

✔ interpret map evidence of human activity
✔ interpret map evidence of tourism.

⭐ **Learning objective**

– To study how to construct sketch maps.

⭐ **Learning outcomes**

→ To construct sketch maps using appropriate scales and annotations.

Sketch maps

Exam Tip

What is the difference between a label and an annotation?

- A label is a simple descriptive point.
- An annotation is a label with more detailed description or an explanatory point.

How to select and construct sketch maps

Many students are daunted by the idea of drawing sketch maps. What must be remembered is that a perfect replica of the map is not expected, just a simple representation of the main features. There is an example of a sketch map on page 31, showing part of the Looe OS map from page 99.

During an exam, you may be asked to draw a sketch map of a particular feature, for example the woodland or the relief and drainage of an area. You must not redraw the whole of the map extract. What you must do is to show all of the features you have been asked for, plus one or two other distinctive features. If you are asked to draw the relief of an area, you could simply shade in the area of land above a certain height. The sketch should be clear and well labelled or annotated depending on the command word in the question.

You should also be able to interpret a sketch map if you are asked questions about one in the examination. This will involve describing and explaining the physical and human geography which can be seen on the sketch map. It is important when interpreting photographs that your writing is coherent and shows good literacy skills in expressing geographical points. The sketch map will be like the original but will contain less detail, therefore you will need to be able to add to the detail in your written answer by interpreting what is there and filling in what has been omitted. For example, height of the land might only be shaded above a certain contour. But the land below that level could also be included in your answer.

How to draw a sketch from a map

- Using a ruler and pencil, draw a frame to the size you want the sketch map to be. This can be the same size as the map or not, but a scale must be included.
- Lightly draw on the grid lines, writing their numbers down the side and across the bottom of the sketch map. These will act as guidelines.
- Draw in the features that are relevant to the question.
- Do not make the sketch map too detailed. It is not necessary to draw every feature, although you may wish to add other features besides the ones indicated in the question. For example, if you were asked to sketch the distribution of settlement in an area, it would be a good idea to include the road network.
- Add appropriate labels and annotations.
- You may wish to use colour. However, in the exam you will be required to only use a pencil/black pen. Therefore, it would be a good idea to practise completing sketch maps without using colours to differentiate between features.

⬆ Figure 15 An incomplete sketch map of part of the Looe extract

Looe map extract (page 99)

ACTIVITIES

Looe map extract (page 99)

1 Trace Figure 15. Use it to complete a sketch map of the woodland west of easting 23.

Warkworth map extract (page 93)

2 Using the OS map, draw a sketch map of the area between eastings 23 to 27, northings 05 to 12. Mark the following on your sketch:
   a The built-up areas of Alnmouth and Warkworth
   b The Rivers Aln and Coquet
   c The coastline and all coastal features
   d Any tourist information features in the area

REVIEW

By the end of this section you should be able to:

✔ draw, label, understand and interpret sketch maps.

STRETCH AND CHALLENGE
. . . .

Cambridge map extract (page 100)

Using the OS map, draw a sketch map for the area between eastings 46 to 51 and northings 64 to 67. Include all the human and physical features you feel are relevant to show what the area is like.

Exam Tip

When answering questions on satellite imagery, follow the points in the section 'Analysing and explaining the data you have collected' on page 85.

Satellite imagery

Satellite imagery is mentioned in this chapter (see page 35). However, it could be used in any part of the examination. The examination paper could provide a map with a satellite image, or part of it, and expect students to be able to interpret, analyse and evaluate geographical information from the image.

ACTIVITY

⬆ **Figure 17** A satellite image of London

Can you locate the river Thames on the satellite image?
Give reasons for your answer.

Ground, aerial and satellite photographs

How to interpret ground, aerial and satellite photographs

Ground photographs are, as the name suggests, ones that are taken when the person is standing on the ground. They can be taken from many different angles and heights but the person is always on the ground. These photographs could be taken of landforms, natural vegetation, land use or settlement.

Aerial photographs can be taken vertical (directly above). If so, they are called 'bird's eye view' photographs because they show a picture taken as if looking down like a flying bird. These are particularly useful when trying to interpret land-use patterns of an area (see Figure 20). Other aerial photographs are oblique (taken from an angle) and therefore show more detail such as the sides of buildings. Figure 18 below shows the difference between vertical and oblique photographs.

A satellite image is a picture of Earth taken from space. Satellite images can show patterns on a large scale such as the lights from urban areas on a continent, or can zoom in to see small details such as cars on a street.

All of these different types of photographs show elements of the landscape which are not found on OS maps, such as types of crops being grown and the different uses of buildings.

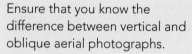

Exam Tip

Ensure that you know the difference between vertical and oblique aerial photographs.

⬆ **Figure 18** The difference between vertical and oblique aerial photographs

⬆ **Figure 19** Oblique aerial photograph of Swanage

⬆ **Figure 20** Vertical aerial photograph of Swanage

Interpretation of aerial photography

When a photograph is interpreted, it involves describing and explaining the physical and human geography which can be seen on the photograph. It is important when interpreting photographs that the writing is coherent and shows good literacy skills in expressing geographical points.

➡ **Figure 21** A satellite photograph of the Swanage area

Example of an interpretation of an aerial photograph

Physical features – relief

The land is very flat with no visible slopes. There are no rivers visible on the photograph. The soil is fertile, therefore a wide variety of crops can be grown.

Human features – land use

Farmland: The fields are large if they are compared with the individual farm buildings shown on the photograph. They are mostly square and rectangular. This implies the use of large arable machinery. It is arable land with a wide variety of crops being grown; this can be seen by the different colours. There are also lines in the fields which show that machinery has been used.

Because crops are growing in most of the fields, the photograph must have been taken in the spring or summer. Most of the fields are divided by roads and ditches with the only exception being tree boundaries in the north-east of the photograph which might be being used as a wind break to protect the village of Landbeach.

Settlement: The village of Landbeach, which is clearly shown to the east of the photograph, is a linear settlement. For the length of the village there is only one house on each side of the road (the road number can be added by reference to the OS map). To the west on the map, there are farms which display a dispersed land-use pattern.

➡ **Figure 22** An aerial photograph of Landbeach near Cambridge and its surroundings

ACTIVITIES

1   Study the different photographs of Swanage shown in
    Figures 19, 20 and 21 and Figure 24 on page 39. What do the
    different photographs show you? It may help to put your answer in
    a table like the one below:

Ground photograph	Oblique aerial photograph	Vertical aerial photograph	Satellite photograph

2   Study the aerial photograph of Warkworth in Figure 27 on page 42.
    Describe the human and physical features of the area.

⬆ **Figure 23** An oblique aerial photograph of Gatwick Airport

Exam Tip

- Photographs are used
  in exams to help you to
  identify features.

- You may also be asked
  to draw a sketch from a
  photograph.

STRETCH AND CHALLENGE
. . . .

Study Figure 23 above, an aerial
photograph of Gatwick Airport.

Draw an annotated sketch of
the photograph.

REVIEW

By the end of this section you
should be able to:

✔ interpret ground, and
  vertical and oblique aerial
  photographs
✔ interpret satellite
  photographs.

Use maps in association with photographs and sketches

Many exam papers have questions which require you to be able to use the OS map with a photograph. The types of questions you could be asked are:

■ recognition of certain features which have been identified by a letter on the photograph
■ the direction the photograph was taken
■ a comparison of features that can be seen on the map and not on the photograph and on the photograph and not on the map
■ the location of where the photograph was taken.

In order to be able to use a photograph with a map, you will have to orientate the photograph so that the features on the photograph are in the same position as those on the map. The map always has north at the top, a photograph may not! The way to do this is to look for an important feature on the photograph, such as the shape of the coastline on the Swanage map (page 104) and Figure 24. Then look at the town shown by the brown shading on the map and the houses on the photograph. It is obvious that the photograph is taken from the north of the map facing south. The exact location is worked out by looking at the fine detail of the photograph in relation to the map; in this case it would be the angle of the coastline, the position of the pier and the headland in the distance. Figure 20 has been annotated with the answers to questions that you might be asked when using a map with a photograph.

Other examination questions may require you to use the OS map to complete a sketch. There also could be sketches drawn with features labelled that you then have to identify using the map. There is an example of this on page 31 where there is a sketch of the Looe map. This has been covered in more detail earlier in this chapter.

⬆ **Figure 24** A photograph of Swanage Bay taken from 040814 facing south

ACTIVITY

Looe map extract (page 99)

Study Figure 25. It is an aerial photograph of Looe.
1   In which direction was the camera pointing?
2   Copy and complete the table below using the photograph and the OS map of Looe on page 99 to help you.

Letter on photograph	Grid reference	Feature
V	Six figure =	Number of road =
W	Four figure =	Name of woodland =
X	Six figure =	Identify symbol =
Y	Four figure =	Name of river =
Z	Six figure =	Identify symbol =

3   State two features that can be seen on the photograph but not on the map.
4   State two features that can be seen on the map but not on the photograph.

↑ **Figure 25** Aerial photograph of Looe

REVIEW

By the end of this section you should be able to:

✔ interpret maps and relate them to photographs
✔ interpret maps and relate them to sketches.

Drawing sketches from photographs

Earlier in this chapter you learnt the difference between a label and an annotation and how to draw sketches from maps. In this section you will learn how to apply your knowledge to sketches. To draw a geographical sketch from a photograph you do not have to be an excellent artist, you just need to follow some basic steps.

How to draw a sketch from a photograph

- Draw a frame to the size you want the sketch to be.
- Lightly draw lines dividing the frame into four quarters. These will help you to draw the rest of the sketch, acting as guidelines. The lines can be erased when the sketch is completed.
- Draw in the most important lines, such as rivers, coastline and the outline of the hills.
- Draw in the less important features, such as woodland, settlements and communication lines. Do not make the sketch too detailed. It is not necessary to draw every feature.
- Add appropriate labels and annotations.
- Rub out the lightly drawn lines that divided the sketch to start off.

The sketch in Figure 26 is a drawing of Warkworth taken from the aerial photograph in Figure 27. It has been given descriptive labels (in blue) and annotations (in red) explaining its site.

No buildings as area is liable to flooding

The river protects the settlement on three sides

Settlement located inside the bend of the meander

Castle built on area of higher ground

River can be used for communication with other settlements

Bridge provides access but can be easily defended

Allotments found on fertile river soils

Area inside the meander is flat, which is ideal for building

River provides drinking water

Castle well positioned to defend the settlement

⬆ **Figure 26** Sketch of Warkworth

Figure 27 Aerial photograph of Warkworth

Figure 28 Photograph of Warkworth from Amble

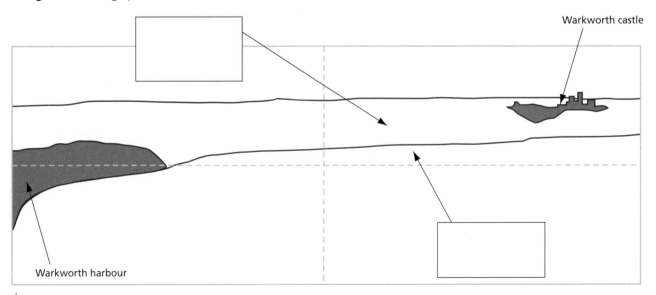

Warkworth castle

Warkworth harbour

Figure 29 Incomplete sketch of Warkworth from Amble

⬆ **Figure 30** Photograph of St Bees in Cumbria

ACTIVITIES

1 Study Figure 28. It is a photograph of Warkworth from Amble. Trace Figure 29 – an incomplete sketch of the photograph. Complete the sketch as directed in the 'how to' box on page 41. The boxes give ideas of where you could add labels.

2 Draw a sketch of Figure 30. Label the following on the sketch:
   a A caravan site
   b Types of coastal defence
   c The beach
   d The cliffs
   e The village of St Bees
   f The Lake District hills in the background

STRETCH AND CHALLENGE

· ·

On your sketch of Warkworth (from question 1 of the Activities), add some annotations to explain the site of Warkworth.

Exam Tip

In exams, you could be asked to complete sketches rather than draw them from scratch.

REVIEW

By the end of this section you should be able to:
✔ draw sketches from photographs and in the field
✔ label and annotate sketches.

Label and annotate diagrams

All geography students need the basic skills of being able to draw, label and annotate diagrams and graphs. These skills will be required to achieve good grades in all geography exams.

Diagrams

Diagrams should be used in geography to demonstrate knowledge. They can be particularly useful where you are required to explain the formation of landforms. For example, the diagram in Figure 31 shows how cliffs retreat. It can sometimes be more appropriate to draw a series of diagrams to show the sequence of something happening.

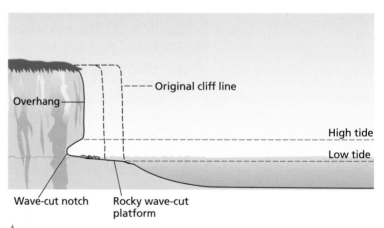

⬆ **Figure 31** Cliffs and wave-cut platforms

Graphical skills

In Chapter 3

Graphical skills you will:

→ study bar charts, histograms with equal class intervals, divided bar charts and population pyramid charts
→ study line graphs, compound line graphs, flow lines, desire lines and isolines
→ study pie charts
→ study pictograms
→ study choropleth maps
→ study proportional circles
→ study scatter graphs
→ study dispersion graphs
→ study star and radial graphs
→ study triangular graphs
→ study kite diagrams.

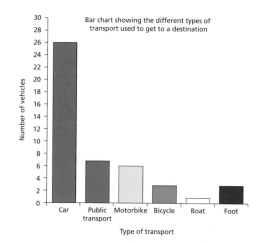

Bar chart showing the different types of transport used to get to a destination

3 Graphical skills

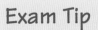

Exam Tip

Remember that bar charts show discrete data; histograms show continuous data.

Different types of bar graphs

What is the difference between a bar chart and a histogram?

There are a number of differences between bar charts and histograms that students need to be aware of. Bar charts are one of the simplest forms of displaying data. Each bar is the same width but of varying length, depending on the figure being plotted. The bars should be drawn an equal distance apart. The data used for a bar chart is discrete data. This means that it is a discrete piece of information. An example would be the different types of vehicles in a traffic count.

When drawing a histogram, the bars should be drawn touching each other because a histogram is used to portray continuous data. An example would be the traffic flow for a continuous time frame.

How to draw a bar chart for the different types of transport used to get to a destination

- Decide on an appropriate scale on the x-axis for the bars. Remember that the bars should be the same width with a gap in between each one. This can be the same width as the data bar or a different width but the width must be a regular size.
- Decide on an appropriate scale on the y-axis for the number of vehicles. Remember that the scale should be spaced out evenly and allow for the highest value in the data set.
- Draw each of the bars to the correct value.
- The bars should be coloured in different colours as the data is discrete.
- Don't forget to label your axes and put a title on your graph.

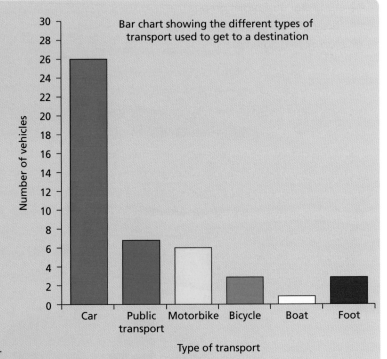

⬆ **Figure 1** Bar chart showing the different types of transport used to get to a destination

How to draw a histogram with equal class intervals of pedestrian flow for a continuous time scale

- Decide on an appropriate scale on the x-axis for the bars. Remember that the bars should be the same width with no gap in between.
- Decide on an appropriate scale on the y-axis for the number of people. Remember that the scale should be spaced out evenly and allow for the highest value in the data set.
- Draw each of the bars to the correct value.
- The bars should be coloured in the same colour as the data is continuous.
- Don't forget to label your axes and put a title on your graph.

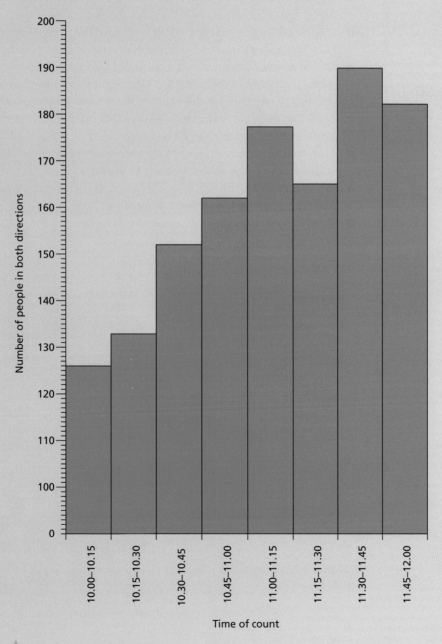

Figure 2 Histogram showing pedestrian flow for a continuous time scale

What is a divided bar chart?

In divided bar charts, the bars are subdivided on the basis of the information being displayed – in this example the sectors of industry in different countries. Each bar is out of 100 per cent.

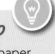
How to draw a compound (divided) bar chart for sectors of industry in certain countries

- These can be drawn with the bars joined or an equal distance apart. In this example the bars are joined together.
- Decide on an appropriate scale on the x-axis for the per cent employed. Remember that the scale should be spaced out evenly.
- Decide on an appropriate width of bar for the y-axis. Remember that the bars should be the same width with no gap in between them.
- Divide each of the bars into the correct percentage for the industrial sector. For example, France has 6 per cent in primary, the line will be drawn at 6 per cent on the graph; 28 per cent in secondary, the line will be drawn at 34 per cent because it builds on the 6 per cent which is already there; tertiary has 66 per cent, which is the rest of the space.
- Each sector, for example primary, secondary or tertiary, should be coloured the same colour in each of the bars.
- When complete, the whole of the graph should be coloured in. In this example, there will be three colours used.
- Don't forget to label your axes and put a title on your graph.

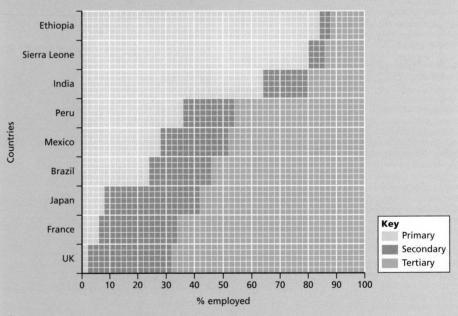

Figure 3 A compound (divided) bar chart showing the sectors of industry in certain countries

What is a population pyramid?

A population pyramid is a form of histogram. It portrays information on age and sex data for a group of people. It is constructed in a number of ways, but usually as 5- or 10-year age groups, with males on one side and females on the other.

The lines are drawn horizontally and are the same width. The length of the bars is determined by the number of people in that age group or the percentage of the total population that age group represents.

How to draw a population pyramid for Cornwall and the Scilly Isles

- Use the graph paper in landscape view.
- Either draw two lines vertically up the centre of the paper a small distance apart, or draw one line as shown in Figure 4.
- The x-axis is now divided into two halves. The left-hand side of the graph paper is for men, the right-hand side is for women. Decide on an appropriate scale for the x-axis. It should be the same for each side of the graph. Remember that the scale should be spaced out evenly and allow for the highest value in the data set.

- Decide on an appropriate width of bar for the y-axis. Remember that the bars should be the same width with no gap in between them.
- Draw each of the bars to the correct value.
- The bars should be coloured in the same colour because the data is continuous.
- Don't forget to label your axes and put a title on your graph.
- You can then add appropriate annotations to explain the information on the pyramid.

Figure 4 Population pyramid for Cornwall and the Scilly Isles

What is a located bar chart?

Bar charts can be placed on to maps to give the data more relevance. In this case, the bar charts have been drawn at the appropriate place on the map. Another way of doing this would be to draw the bar charts on tracing paper and use the tracing paper as an overlay. It is also possible to draw the bar charts on graph paper and paste them on to the map.

ACTIVITIES

1. Draw and complete the population pyramid for Cambridge shown in Figure 5. Use the data in this table and the 'how to' box on page 49 to help you.
2. Describe the shape of the pyramid. Use data in your answer.
3. Give reasons why this is an appropriate technique for this type of data. Choose the two most appropriate statements from the list below.
   - It shows that there is a relationship between the data sets.
   - It clearly shows whether any of the age groups has more of the population than the others.
   - The patterns in the data cannot be clearly seen. The data is discrete.
   - The data is continuous.
4. Describe the pattern of seasonal water supply in the Mediterranean shown in Figure 6. Base your description on the answers to the questions below.
   - What was the highest precipitation in the summer and which country received it?
   - What was the highest precipitation in the winter and which country received it?
   - Which country had the greatest difference between summer and winter totals?
   - What was the amount?
   - Which country had the smallest difference between summer and winter totals?
   - What was the amount?

Age	Males X1000	Females X1000
0–9	5	4
10–19	7	6
20–29	15	12
30–39	8	7
40–49	6	6
50–59	5	4
60–69	3.5	3
70–79	3	4
80–89	1	2.5
90 and over	1	2

Figure 5 Part of the population pyramid for Cambridge

⬆ **Figure 6** Seasonal water supply in the Mediterranean

STRETCH AND CHALLENGE

• •

Use the census to find out population information for your settlement or area in 2001 and 2011.
Draw two population pyramids using the data.
Analyse the information shown.

REVIEW

By the end of this section you should be able to:

✔ construct bar charts, histograms, compound bar graphs and population pyramids
✔ describe and explain the patterns that the graphs show
✔ use the graphs appropriately.

Exam Tip

Remember, on the exam paper you can be asked why a particular graphical technique is appropriate.

⭐ Learning objective

– To study line graphs, compound line graphs, flow lines, desire lines and isolines.

⭐ Learning outcomes

➔ To be able to construct each type of graph.
➔ To be able to describe and explain the patterns that the graphs show.
➔ To be able to suggest appropriate uses of these types of graphs.

Line graphs, compound line graphs, flow lines, desire lines and isolines

What is a line graph?

A line graph is a basic graphical technique used to show changes over time (continuous data). In all line graphs, there are independent and dependent variables. Line graphs can be used to show multiple sets of data, for example traffic counts for the same place at different times.

How to draw a line graph for traffic counts

- The times of the count are the independent variable because the counts are dependent on when they are completed. These should be plotted on the horizontal x-axis.
- The number of vehicles is the dependent variable and should be plotted vertically on the y-axis.
- Decide on a scale appropriate for the range in values to be plotted on the x- and y-axes.
- Plot each line in turn. There should be four lines on your completed graph.
- They should be drawn in different colours and a key provided.
- Don't forget to label your axes and put a title on your graph.

Times	Friday 6 May		Sunday 8 May	
	Into Lulworth	Out of Lulworth	Into Lulworth	Out of Lulworth
12.30–1.00	30	41	117	71
1.00–1.30	42	44	113	76
1.30–2.00	27	41	123	45
2.00–2.30	30	32	136	53
2.30–3.00	23	13	83	72
3.00–3.30	15	10	65	80

Key:
— Sunday into Lulworth
— Sunday out of Lulworth
— Friday into Lulworth
— Friday out of Lulworth

Figure 7 Graph of traffic flows into and out of Lulworth Cove

What is a compound line graph?

In compound line graphs, the graph is subdivided on the basis of the information being displayed in lines across the graph. For example, in Figure 8 the USA's percentage of world usage of renewable fuels has declined from 29 per cent in 1990 to a projected 20 per cent in 2030.

Exam Tip

Remember that you may be asked why a particular graphical technique is appropriate.

How to draw a compound line graph for renewable energy usage

- The years are the independent variable and should be plotted on the horizontal x-axis.
- The percentages are the dependent variable and should be plotted vertically on the y-axis.
- Decide on a scale appropriate for the range in values to be plotted on the x- and y-axes.
- Plot the data for the first country, the USA, on the graph.
- Add the percentage for the second country to the percentage for the first country. This should

be calculated for each year, for example USA in 1990 is 29 per cent; add 14 per cent for Canada. The point for Canada should be plotted at 43 per cent.

- The area between the countries should be coloured in a different colour for each section. Ideally, the order of the countries should be largest to smallest with colours that can be clearly identified.
- Don't forget to label your axes and put a title on your graph.

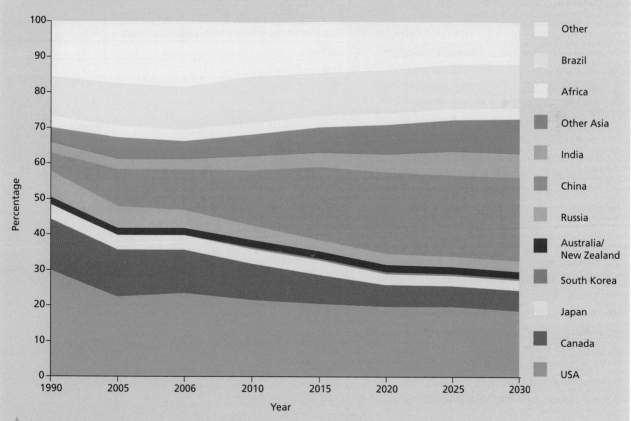

Figure 8 World usage of renewable energy by region 1990–2030 (Source: US Energy Information Administration data)

What is a desire line?

A desire line is drawn to show the direction of movement. The line is drawn from the origin to the destination of a particular movement. For example, traffic flows from the suburbs of a city to the city centre.

What is the difference between a flow line and an isoline?

Flow line maps and isoline maps are more sophisticated ways of portraying data.

A flow line shows movement between places. The thickness of the line indicates the amount of movement. The direction can be shown by an arrow. Figure 9 shows pedestrian flows at a number of places around Windsor town centre. The arrows point in both directions, showing that the total is a combination of both directions.

How to draw a flow line map for pedestrian counts in Windsor

- Draw a base map which shows the relevant details, such as the main roads in the town centre where the counts were carried out. Mark in pencil where the actual counts took place.
- Study the range of the values and decide on an appropriate scale for the width of the arrows. If the scale is too large the flow lines will dominate the map, so take care at this stage to use the appropriate scale. In Figure 9 the scale is 5 mm thickness = 100 pedestrians.
- Draw the flow lines; these should go along the road where the count took place. The tail of the arrow should be where the flow began and the nose should point in the direction of the flow.
- As the count is a combination of both directions, the arrow will point in both directions. If a note had been made of the direction of the count, two arrows should then be drawn, one for each direction.

Street	Pedestrian flow
William Street	210
St Leonards Road	112
High Street	159
Peascod Street (close to Queen Victoria Statue)	166
Peascod Street (close to King Edward Court)	100
Station	112
Thames Street	277

➡ **Figure 9** Pedestrian flows in Windsor

An isoline joins places of equal value and shows the distribution of an item over a particular area. Figure 10 shows places that are equal walking time from a shopping centre; these are known as isochrones. The most well-known isolines are:

- contours, which join places on a map of equal height
- isobars, which join places of equal pressure on a weather map
- isovels, which join places of equal velocity in a river.

How to draw an isoline map for time distance from a retail centre

- Plot the data onto a map of the area. This should be a series of points that have a fairly even spatial distribution.
- Decide on the interval that you want between the isolines. If this is too small, then the map will appear cluttered. If it is too great, the map will become too generalised.
- Draw in your isolines, in this case every 5 minutes.
- The space between the isolines can be left blank or shaded in. If shaded, the colour should become greater as the value becomes higher.
- If you shade your map, then you should provide a key.

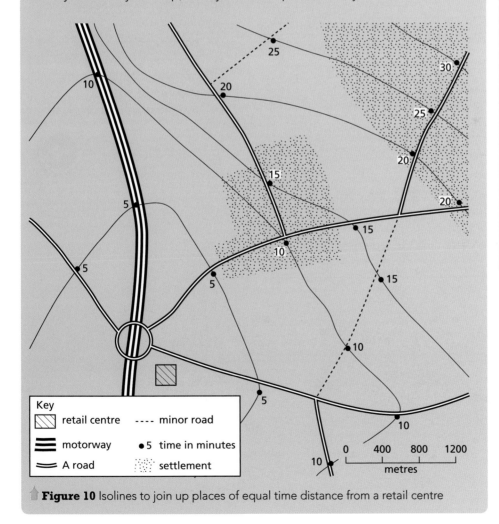

Key
- ◩ retail centre   ---- minor road
- ≡ motorway   •5 time in minutes
- ⟿ A road   ⋯ settlement

Figure 10 Isolines to join up places of equal time distance from a retail centre

Exam Tip

In the exam, it is more likely that you will be asked to complete isoline maps. Remember to draw lines evenly across the map.

You may be asked to complete line graphs or describe the changes that they show.

- Be sure to practise describing the changes, not necessarily the patterns.
- You may be asked to describe one line on a graph that contains a number of lines – be sure to do what the question asks. For example, for a line graph that shows information on primary, secondary and tertiary employment, you may be asked just to discuss the changes in primary industry.

ACTIVITIES

1 Study the line graph for traffic flows in and out of Lulworth Cove on page 52. Suggest two advantages and two disadvantages of this display technique.

2 A line graph is one way of portraying traffic count data. Choose another type of graphical technique.
   a Draw the graph.
   b Give reasons why this is an appropriate technique for this type of data.
   c Describe the pattern shown on the graph.

3 Study Figure 9 on page 54, which is a flow line map of pedestrian counts in Windsor. State four ways in which this map has been incorrectly drawn.

4 Redraw the map of pedestrian flows in Windsor correctly.

5 State another graphical technique that could be used to display this data.

6 Complete a compound line graph for the information in the table below. The table shows different countries' percentage share of the world's gross domestic product (GDP).

	2005	2010	2015	2020	2025	2030
USA	23	22	21	21	20	18
Europe	28	24	22	18	16	13
Japan	10	9	8	6	5	4
China	4	9	12	14	16	18
India	3	4	5	8	10	12
Rest of Asia	6	6	7	8	8	10
South America	6	6	6	6	6	6
Russia	4	4	3	3	3	3
Other	16	16	16	16	16	16

REVIEW

By the end of this section you should be able to:

✔ construct each type of graph
✔ describe and explain the patterns that the graphs show
✔ use the graphs appropriately.

STRETCH AND CHALLENGE

Contour lines are isolines. Trace the drawing and complete it by plotting the following contour lines: 140, 130, 110, 100, 90, 80 and 70. Use Figure 13 on page 27 to determine the type of slope shown on the diagram.

Pie charts

What is a pie chart?

A pie chart or divided circle is a basic graphical technique for showing a quantity which can be divided into parts. A pie chart can also be drawn as a proportional circle. (This is dealt with on pages 62–63.) Pie charts can be located on maps to show variations in the composition of a geographical phenomenon.

How to draw a pie chart for types of employment in rural areas

- If necessary, convert your data into percentages.
- You can either convert your percentages into degrees or use a percentage protractor to draw your pie diagram.
- Draw a circle and mark the centre.
- Subdivide the circles into sectors of the appropriate size.
- Differentiate the sectors by using different shadings or colours.
- Complete a key explaining the shadings and/or colours.
- Don't forget to put a title on your work.

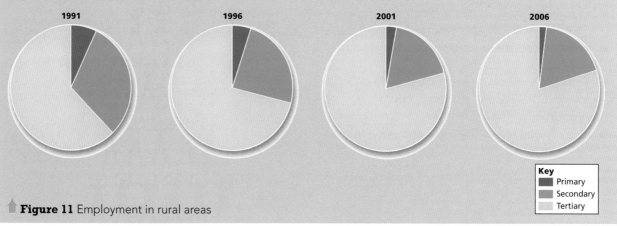

Key
- Primary
- Secondary
- Tertiary

 Figure 11 Employment in rural areas

ACTIVITIES

1 Construct a pie chart for the 2011 data shown in the table.

Type of employment in 2011	Percentage
Primary	2
Secondary	16
Tertiary	82

2 Outline the changes in employment shown between 1991 and 2006 in Figure 11.
3 Suggest another graphical technique that could be used to show this information.

STRETCH AND CHALLENGE

Complete a pie chart for the information below.

Justify your use of this technique.

Type of water consumption	Percentage usage
Domestic	11
Agriculture	69
Industry	20

Exam Tip

You may be required to construct, complete and interpret pie charts.

⭐ Learning objective

– To study pictograms.

⭐ Learning outcomes

➔ To be able to construct pictograms.
➔ To be able to describe and explain the patterns that pictograms show.
➔ To be able to suggest appropriate uses of pictograms.

Pictograms

What is a pictogram?

A pictogram is a way of portraying data using appropriate symbols or diagrams that are drawn to scale. Pictograms can be a useful way of displaying data if accuracy is not so important and the data is discrete.

How to draw a pictogram for world population growth

- Study the data that has to be displayed. Decide on the symbols to use to display the information. In this case the shape of a person could be drawn.
- Decide the scale for the symbols. In this case 1 person = 1 billion people.
- When constructing a pictogram, the years do not need to be continuous.
- Draw the symbols. In some cases the symbol may not be full-sized if it represents a proportion of the full amount.
- Don't forget to provide a key and put a title on your graph.

1804
1927
1960
1974
1987
1999
2011

1 person = 1 billion people

Figure 12 Pictogram for world population growth

ACTIVITIES

1 Construct a pictogram for the data below, which was taken from a questionnaire of how shoppers travelled to a shopping centre.

Mode of transport	Number of people
Car	26
Public transport	7
Taxi	1
Pedal bike	8
Motorbike	3
On foot	5

2 Choose another graphical technique. Display the data using this technique.
3 Suggest two advantages of using a pictogram.
4 Suggest two advantages of using the other technique you have chosen.

STRETCH AND CHALLENGE

Pictograms can be located on maps. Use the data below to draw pictograms on the map of Windsor (refer to the map on page 54 for the location of the streets).

Street	Pedestrian flow
William Street	210
St Leonards Road	112
High Street	159
Peascod Street (close to Queen Victoria Statue)	166
Peascod Street (close to King Edward Court)	100
Station	112
Thames Street	277

Exam Tip

When drawing pictograms, always remember to provide a key for the symbols.

REVIEW

By the end of this section you should be able to:

- ✔ construct pictograms
- ✔ describe and explain the patterns that pictograms show
- ✔ use pictograms appropriately.

Choropleth maps

What is a choropleth map?

A choropleth map is a map that is shaded according to a prearranged key, each shading or colour representing a range of values. The colours should become darker as the numbers increase. There are some inaccuracies in using this technique; one of these is that variations within units are concealed. It also gives a false impression of abrupt changes at boundaries. However, choropleth maps are easy to complete and show a good visual impression of change over space.

How to draw a choropleth map for average precipitation in the UK

- Obtain a base map of the UK.
- Find the range of your values and devise a shading scale.
- You should try to have no fewer than four shading bands and no more than eight.
- The shading should get darker as the value gets higher.
- Complete the map by shading in the areas.
- Draw a key for the map.
- Don't forget to put a title on your map.

Key

Average annual precipitation

- Above 1400 mm
- 901 to 1400 mm
- 651 to 900 mm
- Below 650 mm

0   150
km

Figure 13 UK rainfall

ACTIVITIES

1   Draw a choropleth map for the information on the top ten tourist destinations in 2009, shown in the table. Use the 'how to' box on page 60 to help you.

Destination	Tourist arrivals (millions)
France	81.9
Spain	59.2
USA	56.0
China	54.7
Italy	43.7
UK	30.7
Germany	24.4
Ukraine	23.1
Turkey	22.2
Mexico	21.4

2   Describe the pattern shown by the map.
3   A choropleth map is one way that this data could be displayed. Suggest two advantages and two disadvantages of using a choropleth map for this data.
4   Suggest and complete another data presentation technique that could have been used to display the data.
5   State one way that this technique is more appropriate than a choropleth map and one way that it is less appropriate than a choropleth map.
6   A technique for displaying this data would be a histogram. Why would a histogram be drawn rather than a bar chart?

Exam Tip

Questions could be set on completing a choropleth map and a key. Therefore, be sure that you understand the rules for a successful choropleth map.

STRETCH AND CHALLENGE

Use the data in the table below to draw a choropleth map of the source countries of migrants to the UK from Eastern European countries between 2004 and 2006.

Country	Number of migrants (thousands)
Czech Republic	25
Estonia	10
Hungary	20
Latvia	28
Lithuania	55
Poland	260
Slovakia	40
Slovenia	5

REVIEW

By the end of this section you should be able to:

✔ draw choropleth maps
✔ describe and explain the patterns that choropleth maps show
✔ use choropleth maps appropriately.

Proportional circles

What are proportional circles?

These are circles that are drawn in proportion to the size of the variable being represented. The symbol could be anything – for example, a pictogram a could be used – but is usually – a circle.

How to draw proportional circles on a map

- Find a base map of the area for the values you are displaying.
- Calculate the square root of each of the values (see table opposite). To work out the square root for Spain, put 14 into a calculator and press the square-root key. The answer should be rounded to one decimal place, so 3.7 is accurate enough.
- Use this answer to construct your proportional circle the radius of a circle.
- Study the square-root values to determine the range.

- Determine a scale that suits the range of square-root values. Remember that the circle must fit on the base map. For example, in Figure 14 a scale of 5 mm is used. Multiply each square-root value by 5 to determine the circle size. Therefore, the proportional circle for Spain has a radius of 18 mm.
- Locate the points on the map where you are going to draw your circles.
- Draw the circles and shade or colour them.
- Provide a key for the scale and put a title on your map.

Key

12–14 million

3–4 million

2 million

Irish Republic

Netherlands

Germany

France

Greece   Turkey

USA

Portugal   Italy

Spain

N

Figure 14 Proportional circles showing the number of British tourist visits to overseas tourist destinations

Top ten overseas tourist destinations	Number of British tourist visits (rounded to the nearest million)
Spain	14.0
France	12.0
USA	4.0
Irish Republic	4.0
Italy	3.5
Germany	3.0
Portugal	2.0
Greece	2.0
Netherlands	2.0
Turkey	2.0

Exam Tip

Remember that on the exam paper you can be asked why a particular graphical technique is appropriate.

ACTIVITIES

1 Complete your own map of the top ten tourist destinations above by following the 'how to' instructions opposite.
2 Describe the pattern shown by the map.
3 State two advantages and two disadvantages of this technique.

STRETCH AND CHALLENGE

Complete a proportional circles map for the data in the table. You should draw pie charts for the information about water usage. The circles should be proportional to the gross domestic product in US dollars (GDP $) with the data within them.

Country	Domestic water usage (%)	Agriculture water usage (%)	Industry water usage (%)	GDP ($)
China	12	65	23	5,000
Australia	15	75	10	29,000
Japan	20	62	18	30,000
India	6	89	5	2,900
Russia	19	18	63	9,000
Uzbekistan	5	93	2	1,700
Malaysia	17	62	21	8,500
Sri Lanka	4	93	3	3,700
Afghanistan	3	96	1	700
USA	17	42	41	37,800

REVIEW

By the end of this section you should be able to:

✔ construct proportional circles
✔ describe and explain the patterns that proportional symbols show
✔ use the graphs appropriately.

⭐ Learning objective

– To study scatter graphs.

⭐ Learning outcomes

➔ To be able to construct a scatter graph.
➔ To be able to explain the patterns shown on a scatter graph.
➔ To be able to suggest appropriate uses of scatter graphs.

Scatter graphs

What is a scatter graph?

A scatter graph can be used to show whether there is a relationship (link) between two sets of data. The pattern of the points describes the relationship. After plotting the points, a line known as a best-fit line should be drawn on the graph. This line will indicate the strength of the relationship (correlation) between the two variables (data sets). The pattern will show a positive or negative correlation or no correlation at all. Study the graphs in Figure 16, which show scatter graphs with different correlations.

How to draw a scatter graph to show whether there is a graphical correlation between the width and depth of a river as it moves from its source (site 1) towards its mouth (site 10)

- Decide which is the independent variable and which is the dependent variable. For these two sets of data, there are no independent or dependent variables. However, if you were plotting how depth changes with distance from the source, the distance from the source would be the independent variable and the depth would be the dependent variable.
- Decide on an appropriate scale on the x-axis for the width measurements. Remember, the scale should be spaced out evenly and allow for the highest value in the data set. In this case, ten squares on the graph paper equals 1 metre.
- Decide on an appropriate scale on the y-axis for the depth measurements. Remember, the scale should be spaced out evenly and allow for the highest value in the data set. In this case, five squares on the graph paper equals 10 cm.
- Plot the measurements for each of the sites onto the graph, labelling each site with the correct number.
- Draw a line of best-fit. This is a straight line through the middle of the points that you have plotted.
- Compare the pattern with the standard patterns for the different types of correlations shown in Figure 16.
- What type of correlation have you plotted?
- Explain what this means.

Figure 15 A scatter graph of river width and river depth

ACTIVITIES

1 Draw a scatter graph for the data below. Use the 'how to' box opposite to help you.

Country	Domestic water usage (%)	GDP ($)
China	12	5,000
Australia	15	29,000
Japan	20	30,000
Thailand	9	7,400
Korea	14	17,700
India	6	2,900
Indonesia	8	3,200
Russia	19	9,000
Turkey	15	6,700
New Zealand	48	21,600
Uzbekistan	5	1,700
Malaysia	17	8,500
Sri Lanka	4	3,700
Algeria	25	5,900
Aghanistan	3	700
Sierra Leone	2	500
USA	17	37,800

2 Is there a correlation? What is its nature?
3 Points that are well away from the line of best-fit are known as residuals or anomalies. Are there any residuals or anomalies? If so, circle them on your graph.
4 Describe and give reasons for the pattern that is shown by the graph.

STRETCH AND CHALLENGE

Another way to test for a relationship between sets of data is to use a statistical technique such as Spearman's rank correlation coefficient. Test the statistical correlation between the data given in question 1 using Spearman's test. Information on how to complete this statistical technique can be found in the Stretch and Challenge section in Chapter 1 on page 7.

REVIEW

By the end of this section you should be able to:

✓ construct a scatter graph
✓ explain the patterns shown on a scatter graph
✓ suggest appropriate uses of scatter graphs.

Exam Tip

Remember to always state the type of correlation and explain what it means.

Positive correlation

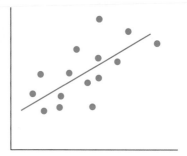

The line of best-fit stretches from the bottom left to the top right of the graph. This indicates a positive correlation; as one variable increases so does the other variable.

Negative correlation

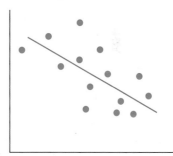

The line of best-fit stretches from the top left to the bottom right of the graph. This indicates a negative correlation; as one variable increases the other variable decreases.

No correlation

The points are distributed all over the graph. This shows that there is no relationship between the variables.

Figure 16 Scatter graphs with different correlations

Dispersion graphs

What is a dispersion graph?

A dispersion graph shows the range of a set of data. It shows whether the data tends to group or disperse. It can also be used to compare sets of data. The values are plotted on the vertical axis. There is also a short horizontal axis, which can show the frequency (the number of times) the variable occurs.

How to draw a dispersion graph for the size of pebbles found on a beach

- The study was completed at three sites, therefore the graph must allow for this.
- Study the values of the pebble sizes in the sample. Decide on a scale for the range of values.
- Plot the scale on the vertical axis.
- The horizontal scale is for the sites and if necessary allows you to repeat a value.
- Don't forget to label your axes and put a title on your graph.
- The mean size has also been marked on Figure 17 using blue diamonds.

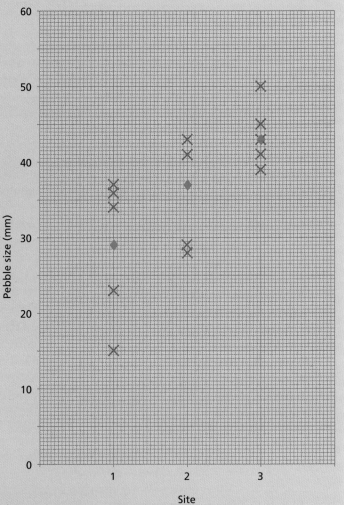

Figure 17 Pebble sizes at three sites on Walton beach

Powers' roundness index

Maurice Powers published a paper in 1953 describing a technique for measuring pebbles. This technique gives a visual representation against which the shape of pebbles can be compared. The chart, now called the Powers' roundness index, is split into six categories, each denoting a degree of roundness from very angular to well rounded. One disadvantage is that one person's opinion on the roundness or angularity of a pebble may differ from another's.

① Very angular   ② Angular   ③ Sub-angular

④ Sub-rounded   ⑤ Rounded   ⑥ Well rounded

Figure 18 Powers' roundness index

STRETCH AND CHALLENGE

Dispersion diagrams can be used to determine the range of data by plotting the inter-quartile range. Plot the median, upper and lower inter-quartile values and the inter-quartile range on the dispersion diagram for river data.

ACTIVITIES

1   Using the information in the 'how to' box opposite, complete a dispersion graph for the data in the tables below. The tables show data on pebble sizes gathered by a group of students from two sites on the Afon Tarell in South Wales.

Site 1

10	5	10	5	12	13	9	12	11	8
10	13	13	14	12.5	13.5	13	15	7	9

Site 2

3	4	6	6	6	5	10	4	7	6
4	6	7	5	3	4	9	3	4	3

2   Outline the differences between the two samples.
3   Describe the pattern shown by the data.
4   Identify another graphical technique that could have been used to display this data.
5   Give reasons for your choice of technique.
6   The students also gathered information on the shape of the pebbles using Powers' roundness index (which gives a value to the shape of pebbles). How could they have displayed this information in the same graph?

REVIEW

By the end of this section you should be able to:

✔ construct dispersion graphs
✔ describe and explain the patterns that the graphs show
✔ use the graphs appropriately.

⭐ Learning objective

– to study star/radial diagrams.

⭐ Learning outcomes

➜ To be able to construct star/radial diagrams.
➜ To be able to describe and explain the patterns that star/radial diagrams show.
➜ To be able to suggest appropriate uses for star/radial diagrams.

Star and radial diagrams

What is a star or radial diagram?

A star/radial diagram consists of straight lines that show movement or a connection between two places. There are several types of these diagrams, including:

- desire lines that show movement from one place to another
- wind roses that have rays originating from the point at which they are being measured. The rays point to the wind direction. The length of the ray is drawn to scale for the amount of days the wind has blown from that particular direction.

How to draw a star/radial diagram (desire lines) for people who shop in Exeter

- Work out the number of people coming from each direction to Exeter.
- Work out a scale that is appropriate for the values in your data.
- Draw the rays of the diagram in the correct direction for the location of the place that the

shoppers came from. This must be to scale. You can do this on paper or on a base map of the area concerned.

- Complete each ray in a different colour.
- You should draw a circle for Exeter with the number 10 (the total number of rays) in the middle.
- Don't forget to provide a key and put a title on your graph.

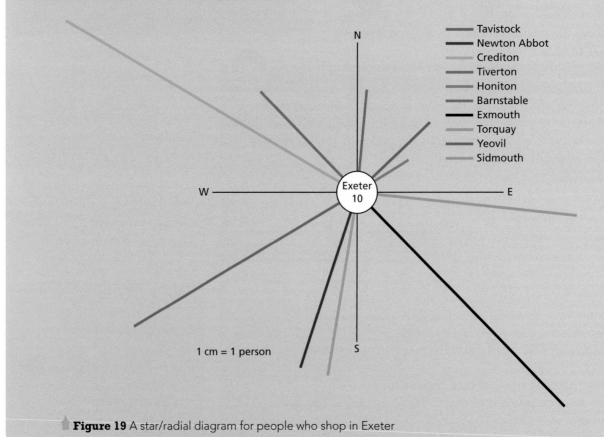

1 cm = 1 person

Figure 19 A star/radial diagram for people who shop in Exeter

ACTIVITIES

1   Construct a radial diagram for the data below. Remember to draw the arrows in the correct direction to where the country is located; even though the information is not being put on to a map, it should be geographically correct.

Top ten overseas tourist destinations from the UK	Number of British tourist visits (millions)
Spain	14.0
France	11.0
USA	4.0
Irish Republic	3.9
Italy	3.5
Germany	3.0
Portugal	2.4
Greece	2.1
Netherlands	2.0
Turkey	2.0

2   Describe the pattern shown by the radial diagram.
3   Suggest reasons why this is a good way of displaying this type of data.
4   Outline another technique that could be used to display this data.
5   Compare and contrast the two techniques in their ability to display this information.

STRETCH AND CHALLENGE

Use the data on the top ten tourist destinations. Complete a star diagram on a suitable map.

REVIEW

By the end of this section you should be able to:
✓ construct star and radial diagrams
✓ describe and explain the patterns that star and radial diagrams show
✓ use star and radial diagrams appropriately.

Triangular graphs

What is a triangular graph?

Triangular graphs have axes on three sides and so they are used to display data that can be divided into three. The data must be in percentages that total 100 per cent. The main advantage is that the graph displays a large amount of data on one chart. It is classed as a sophisticated data technique because it displays information about more than one variable.

How to draw a triangular graph for types of employment in different countries

- There are three axes on the graph. Each axis represents 100 per cent marked at 10 per cent intervals.
- At each 10 per cent interval, lines are drawn at 60° to carry the values across the graph. On

Figure 20 the axes should be labelled primary, secondary and tertiary.

- Plot the data for types of employment in different countries from the table below on to a copy of the triangular graph in Figure 20. Use the arrows around the graph to guide you.
- Don't forget to label your axes and put a title on your graph.

Figure 20 A base chart for triangular graphs

Country	Primary	Secondary (%)	Tertiary (%)
Ethiopia	84	4	12
Sierra Leone	80	6	14
India	64	16	20
Peru	36	18	46
Mexico	28	24	48
Brazil	24	22	54
Japan	8	34	58
France	6	28	66
UK	2	30	68

ACTIVITIES

1 Construct the triangular graph which is explained in the 'how to' box. A base graph has been provided in Figure 20.
2 Describe the pattern shown in the triangular graph you have constructed.
3 Triangular graphs have many advantages and disadvantages. Look at the following statements. Draw up a table headed Advantages and Disadvantages and put the statements below into the correct columns.
   - They are very difficult to construct.
   - They are able to show three sets of data on one graph.
   - They can be confusing if you are unsure which way to read the lines.
   - They have to be constructed for data which adds up to 100 per cent.
   - It is very easy to see the patterns they portray.
   - Anomalies are easy to spot.
   - Base triangles have to be provided because they are very difficult to construct.
   - They can save a lot of time and effort because a lot of information is on one graph.
4 How many pie charts would have to be drawn to portray the same amount of data?

Exam Tip

In the exam you will not have to draw out a complete triangular graph, but you may have to complete one.

STRETCH AND CHALLENGE

Plot the data in the table on page 70 as pie charts on a map of the world.

REVIEW

By the end of this section you should be able to:

✔ construct triangular graphs
✔ describe and explain the patterns that triangular graphs show
✔ use triangular graphs appropriately.

Kite diagrams

What is a kite diagram?

Kite diagrams are usually constructed to show the changes in vegetation species over a particular distance. These are usually the different species that can be found when doing a quadrat survey on a sand dune. The diagram is drawn to show where the quadrat was placed along the transect and the percentage of each species at that point. Therefore, the diagram shows percentage change over a distance. The central line for each 'kite' has a value of '0' and the kite is drawn symmetrically either side of this central line. The information can be on either axis.

How to draw a kite diagram

- Collect the information on vegetation species on a transect line across a sand dune using a quadrat
- On the y-axis, scale out the distance along the transect line.
- On the x-axis, draw the amount of different vegetation found at the various points along the transect. Use the central line as '0' and draw symmetrical kites either side of this line.

Figure 21 A kite diagram

ACTIVITIES

1   Complete your own kite diagram for the information on species below. The locations are 50 metres apart starting from the high tide mark.

Location	Sea couch grass % cover	Marram grass % cover	Bell heather % cover	Birch trees % cover
1	10	2	0	0
2	6	8	0	0
3	2	14	0	0
4	0	10	4	0
5	0	6	50	0
6	0	0	20	40

2   Describe the pattern shown by your kite diagram.
3   State the advantages and limitations of using this technique.

Exam Tip

Kite diagrams can be constructed with the data on either axis. Study the diagrams carefully and work out which is distance and which is vegetation type before answering questions.

Geographical fieldwork skills

In Chapter 4

Geographical fieldwork skills you will:

- → identify questions and routes to enquiry
- → design fieldwork data collection sheets, and collect data with an understanding of accuracy, sample size and procedures, control groups and reliability
- → understand the range of techniques and methods used in fieldwork including both quantitative and qualitative techniques
- → study how to process and present fieldwork data in various ways
- → analyse and explain data using knowledge of relevant geographical case studies and theories
- → write evidenced conclusions from fieldwork notes and data
- → reflect critically on fieldwork data, methods used, conclusion drawn and knowledge gained.

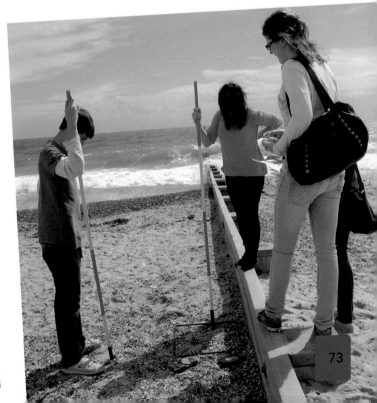

4 Geographical fieldwork skills

⭐ **Learning objective**

– to study geographical fieldwork skills.

⭐ **Learning outcomes**

→ To be able to identify questions/hypotheses and routes to enquiry.

→ To design fieldwork data collection sheets, and collect data with an understanding of the importance of selecting the correct location, accuracy, sample size and procedures, control groups and reliability.

→ To understand the range of techniques and methods used in fieldwork including both quantitative and qualitative techniques.

→ To understand how to process and present fieldwork data in various ways.

→ To analyse and explain data using knowledge of relevant geographical case studies and theories.

→ To write evidenced conclusions from fieldwork notes and data.

→ To reflect critically on fieldwork data, methods used, conclusion drawn and knowledge gained.

Geographical fieldwork skills

Geographical skills will be examined on Paper 3 of the examination. You will need to be able to show your understanding of the processes involved in carrying out a geographical enquiry. You will not be expected to have access to a computer in the exam, but may have to show your understanding of the principles and use of ICT in geographical enquiries. Questions could be asked on how to extract information from the internet or how to use databases such as the census.

Identify questions

All geography students should be able to identify geographical questions. For example, if you look at a particular location, the questions you should be asking yourself are:

- What is the landscape like?
- What are the features that stand out?
- Where is this place – grid references?
- What is the area around it like?
- Why is it like it is?
- What is happening to certain variables?

From asking geographical questions, you should be able to form hypotheses on which a piece of work could be focused. A hypothesis is a statement that can be tested. In an exam question, you might be asked to formulate hypotheses or questions from a sample of information.

A geographical issue is a debatable point. For example, should a wind farm be located in a particular place? Questions such as the following could then be asked:

- What will be the impact on the environment?
- What will be the impact on local people?
- Are the climatic conditions correct?

Hypotheses could be set up and tested, or questions could be set and answered, but it is unlikely that a clear answer will be determined because so many different viewpoints are involved. Issues usually require candidates to make judgements from inconclusive data or evidence.

Whether you are studying a geographical question, hypothesis or issue, you should be able to explain why you are studying it and the results you expect to find out.

You could be given this task question and asked to develop hypotheses or questions to help answer it.
How do channel characteristics vary along a river?

Sample hypotheses for the rivers task question	Sample questions for the rivers task question
• The velocity of the river increases as it moves from its source to its mouth. • The width of the river increases as it moves from its source to its mouth. • The depth of the river increases as it moves from its source to its mouth. • The gradient of the river channel increases as it moves from its source to its mouth. • The wetted perimeter of the river increases as it moves from its source to its mouth.	• How does the velocity of the river change as it moves from its source to its mouth? • How does the width of the river change as it moves from its source to its mouth? • How does the depth of the river change as it moves from its source to its mouth? • How does the gradient of the river channel change as it moves from its source to its mouth? • How does the wetted perimeter of the river change as it moves from its source to its mouth?

The next stage would be to explain why each of the hypotheses/questions are relevant. They may relate to a geographical theory you have been taught.

Establish sequences of enquiry

All geographers should be able to establish a sequence of enquiry. This is sometimes called a road map. What it means is planning out how you will complete your investigation. You must establish what you need to do to answer your task question and the techniques you will need to complete to derive the data you require. You also need to plan when you will be doing each stage of the enquiry and set yourself deadlines. When you write up your study, it should be in the same sequence with each section in a different chapter. There should be good linkage between the chapters, which shows the sequence of the enquiry.

Exam Tip

It is a good idea to use hypotheses rather than questions because often hypotheses are easier to answer.

A brief sample road map for a river study

Planning stage:	location and hypotheses/questions
Data collection:	when should I go on my field trip? what techniques should I use?
Data presentation:	what techniques shall I use?
Analysis:	explaining my results
Conclusions:	answering my questions
Evaluation:	what was the value of my study? how successful were my techniques?

You could be asked to plan the sequence of a geographical enquiry.

Fieldwork data collection

In the examination, you could be asked how you would collect data on a particular topic such as a river or coastal enquiry. You would have to be able to prepare data collection sheets or illustrate ones that you had used in the field. You would have to show awareness of an understanding of the importance of accuracy, sample size, control groups and reliability. You would also need to know about the use of spreadsheets and data-handling software in the field.

Data collection sheets

You can use programmes such as Word™ or Excel™ to produce data collection sheets. These can provide questionnaires and spreadsheets to enable data to be easily collected in the field using tablets, or on mastersheets using a clipboard.

Figure 1 shows an Environmental Quality Analysis (EQA) which has been prepared using a table in Word™. It can be either completed on a mobile device such as a tablet, or printed and completed by hand. Data handling software on data loggers can be used in the field to collect vast amounts of information such as temperature, speed of river flow or simple traffic counts (see Figure 2). The information collected can then easily be transferred onto spreadsheets and displayed.

Exam Tip

You could be asked to define the following terms:

Accuracy – ensuring that a technique/measurement is completed correctly.

Sample size – the number of results that will be acquired.

Control group – the set of data that a student's results could be compared to.

Reliability – ensuring that data is collected consistently.

Criteria	+3	+2	+1	0	–1	–2	–3
Houses – upkeep		x					
Amount of open space			x				
Open space – upkeep		x					
Streets – pavement quality		x					
Streets – road quality			x				
Amount of traffic			x				
Litter – amount	x						
Mechanical noise level	x						
Public noise level	x						
Vandalism – amount	x						
Graffiti – amount	x						
Air pollution – fumes/smells	x						
Derelict	x						

⬆ **Figure 1** EQA, which could be used in an urban or a rural area

⬆ **Figure 2** A data logger. This model can record temperature, sound and light intensity

Sampling

Sample size

The reason why a sample is used, for example a sample of the population, rather than the whole is due to the amount of information that would need to be collected and handled. When deciding how to take a sample and how many samples are needed, the main consideration is how to get a true sample and how to avoid biased information that is really of no use to geography students.

A true sample has enough data to get reliable results – for example, at least five sites on a river of 10 km. For questionnaires, 50 responses is usually seen as a true sample.

Sampling techniques for some fieldwork activities

Measuring river characteristics

Where on a river would you measure its characteristics and how many times would you measure the river characteristics as it flowed from its source to its mouth?

This would depend on the size of the river but the norm would be between five and ten sites. Measurements would be equally spaced along the river's course using an OS map to work out the exact positions – although in practice this may not be possible for practical reasons, such as access to the river bank.

The river course is approximately 10 kilometres long, therefore five sites were chosen.

If access to the river is not possible at that particular point, another site as close to the original as possible should be used.

Study sites are equally spaced along the river's course using an OS map.

Figure 3 Study sites along the Afon Tarell in the Brecon Beacons

Measuring pebble size and shape on a beach

Where on a beach would you measure the pebbles, how often and how many?

The number to measure can be worked out mathematically but it is usually accepted that ten pebbles measured every 50–100 metres, depending on the beach size and just below the high tide line, is a reliable sample site.

An example of how to measure pebble size and shape on a beach.

Measurements should be taken at regular intervals approximately 100 metres between all of the groynes.

Measurements should be taken at the same position in relation to the sea.

A quadrat should be placed on the ground; two stones should be taken from each corner and two stones from the centre at random and then their size and shape recorded.

Figure 4 Study sites along the beach between Bournemouth and Hengistbury Head, Dorset

Questionnaires

How many people should be interviewed?
The number of people to interview will depend on whether you are working alone or in a group but the minimum amount should be 50 people to get a representative sample.

Sampling methods

There are a number of different sampling methods. It is important that before a sample is completed the type of sampling method should be decided upon to give the most accurate result.

Spatial

There are three types of spatial sampling methods.

- Point sampling – this involves choosing particular points and sampling at only these points, for example specific houses down a street or places on a river.
- Line sampling – this involves taking measurements along a line sometimes called a transect, for example a line through sand dunes where vegetation is sampled every 20 metres.
- Quadrat sampling – this involves making a square on the ground and noting down what is in the square, for example the vegetation species at that particular point.

Random

This is where each member of the population has an equal chance of being chosen. It uses random number tables to decide on the sample that is taken.

For example, if the random number table gave us the numbers 8, 6, 4, those would be the houses in the street that would be surveyed in a street survey.

Stratified

This is when the sample contains an equal number of results in each category. This means that the people chosen in the survey are not picked at random. For example, if a questionnaire was being carried out in a tourist resort but the views of both residents and tourists were required, the interviewer would have to ensure that they interviewed both types of people and included in the final results equal numbers of each.

Systematic

In this method, the sample would be collected according to an agreed sample. For example, every fifth person might be interviewed or every tenth house might be used in the street sample.

Opportunistic sampling

This method of sampling occurs when the person collecting the information makes decisions about how the sample will be collected while out in the field. For example, the number of pebbles to be collected for a survey might have to be reduced according the structure of the beach; or the number of people to be interviewed for a questionnaire might be increased if a large number of people were present in the area in that day.

ACTIVITIES

1 Devise hypotheses for the following issue: 'Should a tidal barrage be built in the Severn Estuary?'
2 What would be the sequence of enquiry for a task that was investigating the presence of longshore drift on a beach?
3 Complete the following tasks for the question 'How do river characteristics change as the river flows from its source to its mouth?'

a Identify questions and a sequence of enquiry.
b Design fieldwork data collection sheets.
c Explain your choice of sampling method and sample size for each technique.
4 For one data collection technique you have completed, describe and explain the method.

What techniques and methods can be used to collect information in the field?

Types of measurement used to collect data in river environments

The fieldwork methods explained in Figure 5 are ways that data can be collected in river environments through measurements being taken. These are known as quantitative data collection techniques; numerical data is acquired in this way.

Gradient – a clinometer is used to measure the gradient. A 5 m section of the river is measured out and marked with two ranging poles. The measurement is taken between the two poles and the degrees are noted. If this is completed at each site, the gradient of the long profile of the river can be calculated.

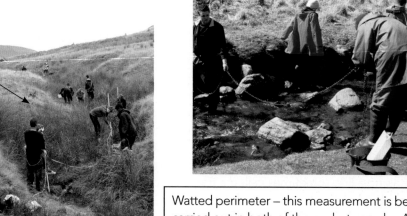

Watted perimeter – this measurement is being carried out in both of these photographs. A chain is laid along the bed of the river and up the banks to the height of the water. The chain is then measured and the distance recorded. This techniques can also be recorded using a tape measure instead of a chain, with people standing on the tape measure. It can also be calculated mathematically from width and depth measurements.

A number of techniques can be seen on this photograph.

Channel width – keep a tape measure just above the current level of the water. Measure from one bank to the other.

River depth – put a tape measure across the river.

Take measurements at regular intervals across the river channel using a metre stick or a ranging pole and tape measure.

These two measurements can then be used to calculate the cross-section area of the river.

Bedload size and shape – bedload size is measured using a calliper. The rock is placed in the calliper and a measurement is read off the side. The shape is determined using Powers roundness index.

Velocity – measure 10 m along the river and place a ranging pole at each end. Drop an orange into the water before the first pole. Start timing as the orange passes the first pole and stop timing when it passes the second pole. Complete this ten times at different place across the river and take the average measurement.

⬆ **Figure 5** Methods of collecting quantitative data through fieldwork

Types of measurement used to collect data in coastal environments

The methods explain in Figure 6 are ways that data can be collected in coastal environments through measurements being taken. These are known as quantitative data. Collection data and numerical data is acquired in this way.

Beach morphology measured through beach profiles – these are completed using ranging poles and a clinometer. Start by the sea and measure the angle between two ranging poles every 10 m until the cliff face is reached.

Measuring the speed and direction of longshore drift – an orange is thrown into the sea. A ranging pole is placed on the beach close to the sea at this point and a stopwatch is started. It was stopped after five minutes had passed. The distance the orange had travelled was then measured with a tape measure. The test was repeated five times to get an average speed.

Sediment characteristics, the size and shape of pebbles – this is usually completed with a beach profile. A quadrat is placed on the ground (if it is not available two metre rules will be fine) where each ranging pole is placed. Ten stones are picked, two from each corner and two from the middle. They are measured with a calliper and their shape is checked against Powers roundness index.

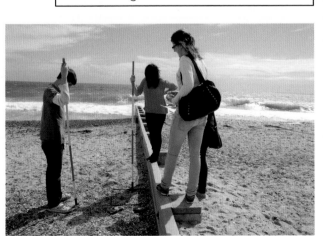

Measuring the build up of beach material beside groynes to check for longshore drift – the depth of sand is measured on either side of the groyne. This is done at two points along the groyne, in the middle of the groyne and next to the sea wall. This is repeated on all the groynes on the beach.

Figure 6 Quantitative data collection methods

Types of measurement used to collect data in urban environments

In urban environments, a number of techniques can be used to measure features. Shop frontage can be measured to see whether the size of the shop front changes with distance from the centre of the city. A land-use survey could be completed. A transect is carried out down streets leading from the centre of the city. Students walk down a street noting down the land-use function of the buildings on a map using the key shown in Figure 7. Information is shared and numerous data handling and analysis techniques can be carried out on the information collected. A bi-polar analysis can also be completed to assess the environmental quality of an area shown on Figure 8.

Land use	Code
Residential	R
Industrial	I
Commercial (including retail)	C
Entertainment	E
Public buildings	P
Open space	O
Transport	T
Services	S

Figure 7 Land-use survey form

Negative	1	2	3	4	5	Positive
There is lots of litter						There is no litter
Noisy						Very quiet
Lots of dog fouling						No dog fouling
No hanging baskets or greenery						Lots of greenery
Shop fronts are run down and dirty						Shop fronts are newly painted and well maintained
Shop windows are dirty						Shop windows are clean
Lots of traffic						Pedestrianised area
Few shoppers						Many shoppers
Buildings are old and not cared for						Buildings are new and modern

Figure 8 Environmental quality survey form

Techniques that use observation to collect information in the field

Other methods of data collection are through observation. These methods are known as qualitative techniques and reflect people's opinions of an area. They usually involve a description or comment about somewhere. These methods can be used to record features that make up the river, coastal or urban landscape. This type of data is collected using techniques such as photographs, sketches or questionnaires.

Photographs and sketches

Photographs are taken in the field of the area under discussion. Descriptions are put on to the photographs back in the classroom. Photographs show a more accurate view of an area but students must ensure that they record the annotations they want to add later. It is often a good idea to sketch and photograph the same area. Satellite images, aerial and oblique aerial photographs can also be used as secondary data in fieldwork enquiries.

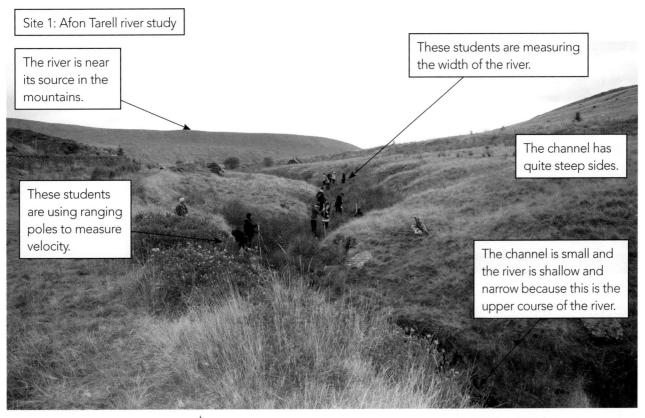

Site 1: Afon Tarell river study

The river is near its source in the mountains.

These students are measuring the width of the river.

The channel has quite steep sides.

These students are using ranging poles to measure velocity.

The channel is small and the river is shallow and narrow because this is the upper course of the river.

Figure 9 Annotated photograph of the river study area

Recurved sea wall to protect the settlement behind the dunes.

Rip rap to dissipate the power of the waves before they reach the sea wall.

Coastal defence techniques have successfully kept the beach in place.

Offshore reef made of rocks to protect the beach behind them.

Figure 10 Annotated field sketch of Sea Palling

Sketches are drawn in the field with annotations and are usually then redrawn in the classroom to improve the presentation. These techniques can be used to provide visual evidence of how river processes impact on people living in an area.

Questionnaires

Another qualitative technique is a questionnaire. This can have closed or open questions, but all of them require the respondent to make a judgement or give an opinion/observation on something. The evidence collected is therefore subjective. A questionnaire can be compiled and completed individually or in groups.

Techniques for processing and presenting fieldwork data

Data that has been collected in the field first has to be processed to make it accessible to all. The usual way is to collate it onto spreadsheets and store it on a computer database for all to be able to access. Once this has been completed, there are many ways that the data can be presented. The data can be used to construct graphs or located onto maps of the study area using software packages which provide students with the ability to layer their information. Diagrams could also be drawn to portray information gained or sketch maps drawn of areas to indicate visual information that has been collected. Analytical calculations can also be completed on data, for example, working out the cross-sectional area and river discharge or scatter graphs completed of pebble size and pebble shape. Other statistical calculations such as means, modes and medians or percentage increase or decrease can also be used to process evidence. Examples of presentation techniques that can be used are in the table below.

Technique	Example
Cartographic	A map of the study area Data placed on a map as proportional circles
Graphical, simple	Bar charts Line graphs Pie charts
Graphical, more complex	Choropleth maps Flow line maps Scatter graphs Transects
Visual	Photographs Field sketches
Analytical calculation	Work out the cross-sectional area and river discharge. Spearman's rank correlation co-efficient for pebble size and shape. Mean, mode, median Percentage increase or decrease

How to calculate cross-sectional area and river discharge

Cross-sectional area

This is calculated by using width and depth measurements. There are two ways to do this: either multiply the width by the depth (you may need to find the mean of the depth measurements first), or plot the width and depth measurements on to graph paper, as shown in Figure 11, keeping the same scale for each of the axes. The squares where the water is shown are then counted to calculate the measurement, which is in square metres.

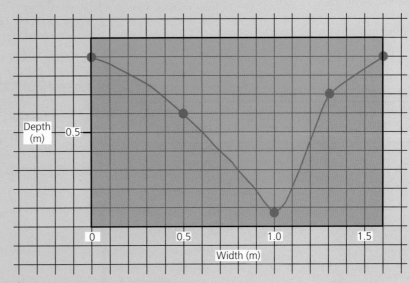

↑ **Figure 11** Cross-sectional area.

River discharge

Discharge is calculated by multiplying the cross-sectional area by the mean velocity for each site. For example, if the mean velocity is 0.95 metres per second and the cross-sectional area is 1.50 m²: Discharge = 0.95 × 1.50 = 1.42 m³ per second (or cumecs).

Analysing and explaining the data you have collected

During fieldwork, you will accumulate a large amount of data that will need to be analysed and explained. This is good practice for the types of questions that you could be asked on paper 3 of the examination. In the examination, you could be asked to explain your own data or be given similar data to explain and analyse. Therefore it is important that you develop skills to do this. If you are asked to analyse, follow these points.
- Describe what you see.
- Ensure that you have included important facts such as dates or numbers or even names.
- Give reasons for the patterns that you see in the data.
- Try to link your reasons to other data that you have collected or to relevant geographical case studies or theories you have studied.

This is a descriptive comment about the map, and contains data about the counties that people came from.

Choropleth to show which county most people came from

1-2 people
3-4 people
5-6 people
7-8 people

1. Dorset. 2. Berkshire. 3. Kent. 4. Yorkshire.
5. Lincolnshire. 6. Derbyshire. 7. Hampshire.
8. Wiltshire. 9. Essex. 10. Nottinghamshire.
11. Greater London. 12. Buckinghamshire.
13. East Sussex. 14. Oxfordshire. 15. Surrey.
16 Tyne and Wear. 17. Hertfordshire.

The choropleth map shows where people who were interviewed came from. The people were visiting Lulworth Cove on Sunday 10th May. According to the map, 7–8 people of the ones interviewed came from Dorset and Berkshire. 1-2 people came from 10 of the counties.

The choropleth map shows where people who were interviewed came from. The people were visiting Lulworth Cove on Sunday 10th May. According to the map 7–8 people of the ones interviewed came from Dorset and Berkshire. A large number of people came from Dorset because Lulworth Cove is in Dorset and therefore they did not have far to travel.

A large number of people interviewed also came from Berkshire, this is because we interviewed a lot of people who came on the trip with us.

This comment about the map contains data about the counties that people came from and analytical comments to explain the data.

Figure 12 Example of student's work. A question might ask you to describe and interpret a choropleth map

Writing conclusions from evidence using your fieldwork notes and data

The conclusion is when you return to your original hypotheses or questions and answer them using the evidence you have provided in the study. The more evidence you use to back up your findings, the more plausible they will be. On paper 3, you could be given some findings and asked to answer a question based on those findings.

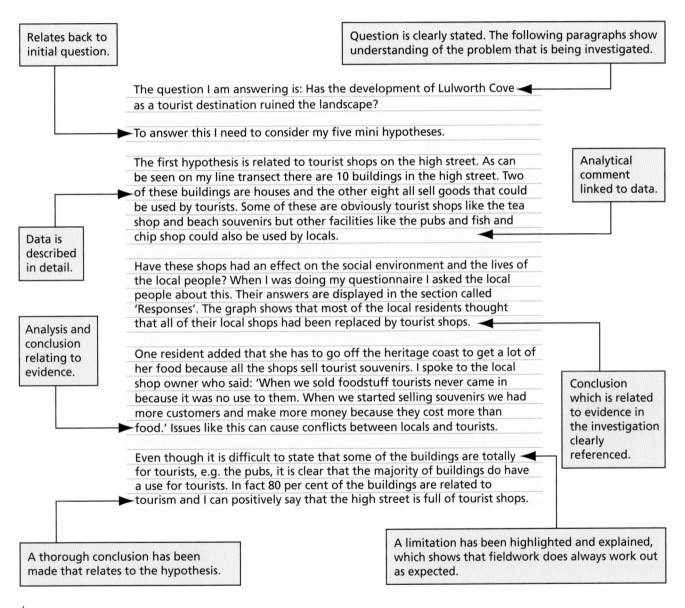

Relates back to initial question.

Question is clearly stated. The following paragraphs show understanding of the problem that is being investigated.

The question I am answering is: Has the development of Lulworth Cove as a tourist destination ruined the landscape?

To answer this I need to consider my five mini hypotheses.

The first hypothesis is related to tourist shops on the high street. As can be seen on my line transect there are 10 buildings in the high street. Two of these buildings are houses and the other eight all sell goods that could be used by tourists. Some of these are obviously tourist shops like the tea shop and beach souvenirs but other facilities like the pubs and fish and chip shop could also be used by locals.

Analytical comment linked to data.

Data is described in detail.

Have these shops had an effect on the social environment and the lives of the local people? When I was doing my questionnaire I asked the local people about this. Their answers are displayed in the section called 'Responses'. The graph shows that most of the local residents thought that all of their local shops had been replaced by tourist shops.

Analysis and conclusion relating to evidence.

One resident added that she has to go off the heritage coast to get a lot of her food because all the shops sell tourist souvenirs. I spoke to the local shop owner who said: 'When we sold foodstuff tourists never came in because it was no use to them. When we started selling souvenirs we had more customers and make more money because they cost more than food.' Issues like this can cause conflicts between locals and tourists.

Conclusion which is related to evidence in the investigation clearly referenced.

Even though it is difficult to state that some of the buildings are totally for tourists, e.g. the pubs, it is clear that the majority of buildings do have a use for tourists. In fact 80 per cent of the buildings are related to tourism and I can positively say that the high street is full of tourist shops.

A limitation has been highlighted and explained, which shows that fieldwork does always work out as expected.

A thorough conclusion has been made that relates to the hypothesis.

▲ **Figure 13** Analysis and conclusions

Reflecting critically on your data, methods, conclusion and knowledge gained

After completing your fieldwork, it is important to evaluate or state the value of the data collection techniques, the data presentation techniques and the study as a whole – in other words the evidence you have managed to find. This will prepare you for possible questions on paper 3.

In paper 3, you may be asked to do an evaluation of a particular type of data collection or presentation technique. You may also be asked to evaluate the findings of a particular study. When completing evaluations, it is always a good idea to focus on how things could be improved or the problems experienced and how you might solve them. Questions on data collection techniques could be linked to your fieldwork by asking you to reflect critically on a technique you have carried out.

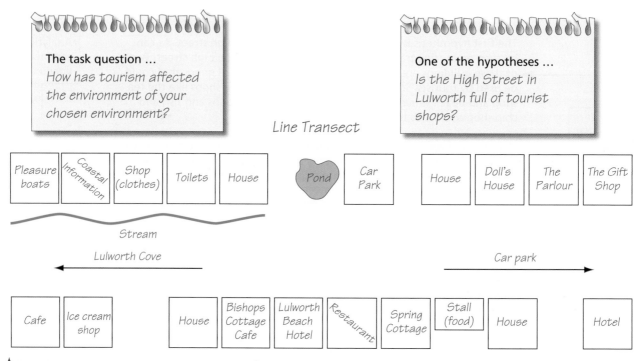

↑ **Figure 14a** Example of a student's work. A question might ask you to draw conclusions from evidence and evaluate methods of data collection, presentation and analysis

The data collection method ...

The data was collected by walking down the High Street noting down what was on either side. A category chart with a key was used, which helped to identify the different shops. The key meant that we had room on our chart to fit everything in. Each person did their own transect because they could have interpreted the High Street in different ways.

Evaluation of the method ...

This is a good way of collecting the data because it would be very reliable as it was primary data collection. However, I did have problems giving all of the shops a category; I asked other members of my group for help.

Here the method of data collection is explained and evaluated.

The data presentation method ...

I drew out each of the buildings on the High Street and wrote in the box what it was. I marked clearly which end of the street was near the car park and which end was by the beach.

Evaluation of the method ...

This method could have been improved if I had drawn everything to scale. The road would then have been the correct length and the buildings would have represented their actual size. I could then have assessed their importance to the area. I should also have taken photographs of the buildings to help explain their use.

Here the method of data presentation is described and evaluated.

The analysis of your findings ...

The line transect shows that there are many tourist related shops in the High Street. They provide food and souvenirs for the tourists, there were no shops that provided for the local community.

A simple analytical comment which uses the evidence on offer to put forward a viewpoint.

A simple concluding comment. In normal circumstances, more than one technique should be used to draw concluding comments.

Concluding the hypothesis ...

From the evidence of the line transect, the High Street is full of tourist shops. Therefore the tourists are having an impact on the character of Lulworth Cove.

⬆ **Figure 14b** An example of a student's work on analysing and drawing conclusions from evidence.

ACTIVITIES

1 Using your own experience in the field, state your hypotheses and write a conclusion drawing on evidence from your findings.

2 The following are the results of traffic counts taken at Lulworth Cove in Dorset. The students were trying to discover whether the day of the week or time was important for the numbers and types of traffic recorded.

   a Analyse the data in the tables.

   b What conclusions can you draw from this evidence?

Traffic counts – Friday

Time	Out of Lulworth						Into Lulworth					
	Cars	Lorries	Coach/bus	Bike	M/bike	Total	Cars	Lorries	Coach/bus	Bike	M/bike	Total
12.30–1.00	19	9	2	0	0	30	31	8	1	1	0	41
1.00–1.30	42	0	0	0	0	42	40	2	0	0	0	42
1.30–2.00	27	0	0	0	0	27	37	2	2	0	0	41
2.00–2.30	27	1	2	0	0	30	29	2	0	0	1	32
2.30–3.00	20	1	0	1	1	23	13	0	0	0	0	13

Traffic counts – Sunday

Time	Out of Lulworth						Into Lulworth					
	Cars	Lorries	Coach/bus	Bike	M/bike	Total	Cars	Lorries	Coach/bus	Bike	M/bike	Total
12.30–1.00	107	0	3	4	3	117	65	0	5	1	0	71
1.00–1.30	108	0	3	1	1	113	75	0	1	0	0	76
1.30–2.00	131	0	0	0	2	133	45	0	0	0	0	45
2.00–2.30	131	1	0	0	4	136	56	2	2	3	0	63
2.30–3.00	82	0	0	0	1	83	69	0	1	1	1	72

REVIEW

By the end of this section you should be able to:

✔ identify questions/hypotheses and routes to enquiry

✔ design fieldwork data collection sheets, and collect data with an understanding of the importance of selecting the correct location, accuracy, sample size and procedures, control groups and reliability

✔ understand the range of techniques and methods used in fieldwork including both quantitative and qualitative techniques

✔ study how to process and present fieldwork data in various ways

✔ analyse and explain data using knowledge of relevant geographical case studies and theories

✔ write evidenced conclusions from fieldwork notes and data

✔ reflect critically on fieldwork data, methods used, conclusion drawn and knowledge gained.

OS maps and questions

Chapter 5 contains sections of OS maps at different scales and examination-style questions:

→ Warkworth map 1:50 000
→ Wensleydale 1:50 000
→ New Forest 1:25 000
→ Looe 1:50 000
→ Cambridge 1:50 000
→ Swanage 1:50 000, 1:25 000

5 OS maps and questions

Warkworth map

1 Study Figure 1. It is a photograph taken at grid reference 248063.

    a In which direction was the camera pointing? **(1 mark)**

    b Name the river flowing under the bridge.
      i Warkworth
      ii Hermitage
      iii Aln
      iv Coquet **(1 mark)**

2 Match the coastal feature to the correct grid reference. **(3 marks)**

    flat rock, dunes, beach

    2507   2611   2605

3 Study Figure 2. It is a sketch map of part of the OS map extract on page 93. Trace a copy of the sketch map. Label the following features on the sketch map. You should use the correct symbol and provide a key.

⬆ **Figure 1** A photograph of Warkworth

    a Alnmouth station **(1 mark)**
    b Public house **(1 mark)**
    c Post Office **(1 mark)**
    d Complete the road network on the map by adding the A1068, the B1339 and the B1338. **(2 marks)**

4 Describe the course of the River Aln shown on the sketch map. **(4 marks)**

5 A family are on holiday staying at Hermitage Farm in grid square 2406. They would like to visit Warkworth for lunch and then go onto Alnwick castle in the afternoon. Describe their route. **(4 marks)**

⬆ **Figure 2** An incomplete sketch map of Warkworth

Warkworth 1:50 000

Wensleydale map

1   Study the OS map of Wensleydale on page 95 and Figure 3. It is a photograph taken at grid reference 876906.
   a   Name the river shown in the photograph.
      i   Ure
      ii   Hardraw Force
      iii Bain
      iv   Brown **(1 mark)**
   b   In which direction is the river flowing?
      i   east to west
      ii   north to south
      iii west to east
      iv   south to north **(1 mark)**

2   Copy and complete the following table by ticking (✔) in the box if Hawes (8789) and Bainbridge (9390) have that service. **(4 marks)**

Service	Hawes	Bainbridge
Public house		
Place of worship with a spire		
Visitor centre		
Post Office		

3   Identify three pieces of evidence which show that tourism is important in this area. **(3 marks)**
4   In which of the following grid squares is the gradient of the land steepest? **(1 mark)**

      9182   9385   8985

5   State the difference in height between the river valley at 881906 and the spot height at 881923. **(1 mark)**
6   Most of the settlements in the area are located in the river valleys. Suggest reasons why. Use evidence from the map in your answer. **(4 marks)**
7   Contrast the valley of the River Ure between grid reference 880905 and 900903 with the valley of Cragdale Water between grid reference 919840 and grid reference 911855. **(5 marks)**

⬆ **Figure 3** A photograph of a meander bend in Wensleydale

New Forest map

1   Study the OS map of the New Forest on page 96 and Figure 4 on page 78. It is a photograph taken at grid reference 174906. In which direction was the camera pointing? **(1 mark)**
2   Give three pieces of map evidence to show that this area is important to tourists. **(3 marks)**
3   State one characteristic of the course of the River Stour in grid square 1492. **(1 mark)**
4   Describe the physical landscape of the area east of westing 16. **(3 marks)**
5   State one reason for the shape of the coastline east of westing 16. **(1 mark)**

Wensleydale 1:50 000

New Forest 1:25 000

Looe map

1 Study the OS map of Looe on page 98 and Figure 4. It is a photograph taken in grid square 2552 facing south.
   a What is the name of island S? **(1 mark)**
   b What is feature T? **(1 mark)**
2 Suggest reasons for the site of Pelynt. **(4 marks)**
3 Study the OS map of the Looe area.
   a Draw a cross-section from the triangulation pillar 168 in grid square 2261 to Lametton Mill at 260610. You may use the one in Figure 5 on page 98 to help you.

   b Label on the cross-section: East Looe River, B3254, railway line, non-coniferous woodland. **(5 marks)**
4 Study the OS map of Looe and Figure 6. It is a photograph taken in grid square 2552 facing north. There is information on the map that is not on the photograph.
   a State three pieces of information that are present on the map but not the photograph. **(3 marks)**
   b State one piece of information that is on the photograph and not the map. **(1 mark)**

⬆ **Figure 4** A photograph of the coastline near Looe

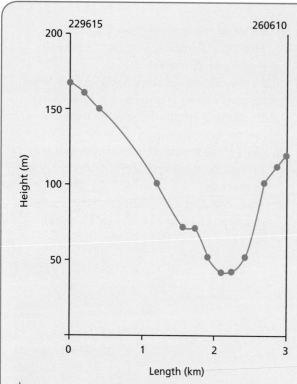

Figure 5 Cross-section from 229615 to 260610

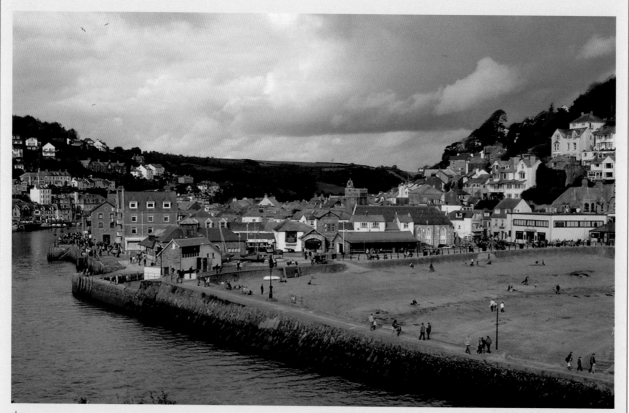

Figure 6 A photograph of Looe

Looe 1:50 000

Cambridge 1:50 000

Cambridge map

1 Study Figure 7. It is an aerial photograph of an area of housing in Cambridge. Also study the OS map on page 100.

   a A number of grid squares are shown in the photograph. Choose the correct one from the following list: 4460, 4657, 4856, 4458. **(1 mark)**

   b What is the railway feature identified by the X? **(1 mark)**

   c Give the six-figure grid reference for the college identified by feature Y. **(1 mark)**

   d What is the number of the road marked Z? **(1 mark)**

   e Describe the pattern of housing identified by the red square on the photograph. Copy out the three following statements that best describe the housing identified by the red square:
   - The houses are in cul-de-sacs.
   - The housing is in a grid-iron pattern.
   - The streets have curves.
   - The houses are in blocks.
   - There are lots of deadends.
   - The streets are in a line.
     (3 marks)

2 Figure 8 is a photograph which was taken above Cherry Hinton (4856).

   a Compare the housing patterns shown in Figures 7 and 8. **(3 marks)**

   b Suggest one reason for these differences. **(1 mark)**

3 Copy and complete the table by identifying features that can be seen on the map and not on the photographs and features that can be seen on the photograph and not on the map. **(2 marks)**

	On map not on photograph	On photograph not on map
Feature 1		
Feature 2		

4 Describe the distribution of 'park and ride' sites shown on the map. **(3 marks)**

Figure 7 Aerial photograph of housing in Cambridge

Figure 8 Aerial photograph of Cherry Hinton

Swanage 1:25 000

▲ Swanage 1:50 000

Swanage map

1 Study the OS map of Swanage on page 104. A family are on holiday in the area shown on the OS map. They are staying near Corfe Castle in grid square 9582. They wish to go out for the day to visit Studland and Swanage. Answer the following questions about their route and the features they see on the way.

  a What is the number of the road which leads from Corfe Castle to Studland?
    i A351
    ii B3351
    iii B3069
    iv A3351 **(1 mark)**

  b They park close to the Post Office in Studland. Which one of the following is the six-figure grid reference of the Post Office?
    i 025822
    ii 038826
    iii 035822
    iv 822035 **(1 mark)**

  c They walk in an easterly direction to Old Harry. Which one of the following owns Old Harry?
    i Harry Thompson
    ii National Trust
    iii Swanage council
    iv National Term **(1 mark)**

  d The family leave Studland and drive to Swanage. In Ulwell they pass a tourist feature. Which tourist feature do they pass in Ulwell? **(1 mark)**

  e They decide to return to Corfe Castle by train. Choose how many stations there are on the Swanage railway from the following:
    i 3
    ii 4
    iii 5
    iv 6 **(1 mark)**

2 Complete the sentences to compare the shape of Harman's Cross in grid square 9880 with that of Worth Matravers in grid square 9777. Use some of the terms in the box.

| B3351 | nucleated | junction | A351 | linear |

Harman's Cross is a … village. Most of the houses are either side of the main … road. The village of Worth Matravers has a more … shape with the houses being grouped around a …
(3 marks)

3 Study Figure 9. It is a photograph of Swanage Bay. Draw a sketch of the photograph. Label the following on the sketch (you will also need to refer to the OS map).
  a the town of Swanage
  b the beach
  c the groynes on the beach
  d Swanage Bay
  e Peveril Point
  f the pier
  (6 marks)

⬆ **Figure 9** A photograph of Swanage Bay

Answers

Chapter 1 answers, pages 2–9

Answers to activities

Page 3
1500 × 1200 = 1,800,000 square metres (m²)

Page 6
1 **a** 290

    b 314

2 **a**

Site	Mean	Mode	Median
1	7.4	7.75	7.75
2	7.5	7.5	7.5
3	6.2	6	6
4	6.5	6.5	6.5
5	6.45	6	6.25
6	4.5	4.5	4.5
7	3.4	3	3.25
8	3.5	2	3.25

  b

Technique	Advantages	Disadvantages
Median	• Easy to calculate • Not distorted by extreme results	• Does not take into consideration precise values
Mode	• Easy to calculate	• Not very useful if the sample size is small
Mean	• Uses all the data so is very inclusive	• Extremes can be a problem if the sample size is small

Page 7
1 Width of 6.6 m

    Width of 8.3 m

2 250 per cent

Page 9
On average, the further from the groyne, the smaller the **pebble size.**

Chapter 2 answers, pages 10–44

Answers to activities

Page 13
1 The tropical rainforests are found either side of the Equator within the Tropics. The continent with the largest rainforest area is South America (Brazil). Europe does not have any rainforests.

2 The higher land is found to the north and west of Great Britain. It is more evenly spread in Ireland. The land above 1,000 m is mainly found in Wales and Scotland with none found in the south and east of Britain. The highest land in England is in the south-west and north of the country.

3 names of mountainous areas, cities

4 The countries with the highest migration change are in southern Europe, including Spain and Italy. The countries with the lowest migration change are in northern Europe, including Sweden and Finland. Ireland, in north-western Europe, is an exception to this rule.

Page 14
1 50°43'N 3°31'W

2 Plymouth

3 A great variety of answers could be given, students working in pairs.

Page 15
1 A 1008

    B Between 1008 and 1012

    C Between 1000 and 1004

2 Weather conditions London
- Wind speed – calm
- Temperature – 28
- Rainfall – none
- Pressure – between 1008 and 1012
- Cloud cover – 2/8 covered

3 Weather conditions Glasgow
- Wind speed – between 23 and 27
- Wind direction – southeast
- Temperature – 15
- Rainfall – rain
- Pressure – below 1000
- Cloud cover – 6/8 covered

4 Bath is behind the depression but there is still 6/8 cloud cover. It is raining with a strong westerly wind between 23 and 27 knots. Lowestoft is in the warm sector. The sky is clear and there is a small breeze of between 13 and 17 knots from the southeast.

Page 17

1 Answer will be different for each student.

2 They condense the information allowing more information to be shown in a small space. They allow inaccuracies.

3 **a** At Waterloo, take the Northern Line. Go through six stations. Get off at the seventh station, which will be Euston. Details of stations in between may be given.

   b Go to Embankment on the District Line. Change to the Northern Line and go north to Tottenham Court Road. Change to the Central Line, go east to Liverpool Street. Details of stations in between may be given.

4 You have no idea of the exact direction on the ground that you are travelling. You have no idea of the distance you have travelled, as no scale is given.

Page 21

1

Symbol	Feature
TH	Town Hall
⚝	Viewpoint
⟨⟩····⟨⟩	Tunnel
⌃ ⌃ ⌃	Electricity transmission line
🙶🙷	Non-coniferous woodland
CH	Club house

2

Symbol	Key	Four-figure reference	Six-figure reference
✝	Place of worship with tower	5683	567833
P	Post Office	5885	587857
△	Triangulation pillar	5884	582847
⌐	Golf course or links	5785	571853
□ Home Fm	Home Farm	5583	551839
➥	Bus or coach station	5685	568858
□ Sch	School	5784	571841

3

Feature	Symbol
Flat rock	🪨

4 National Trust (always open)

5 coniferous

6 PH – Public House, P – Post Office, place of worship (church) with tower.

7

Tourist feature	Grid reference
Information	187133
Caravan site	190119
Camp site	190121
Parking	187142
(Alnwick) Castle	189138
Museum	196122

8 north-west

9 south

10 south-west

Page 23

Wensleydale

1 13.4 cm, 6.7 km   **4** 0.4 km

2 12.6 cm, 6.3 km   **5** 10.8 cm, 5.4 km

3 the river

Swanage

6 14.6 cm, 7.3 km

7 The A road distance is 10.2 cm, 5.1 km. Therefore, the B road is longer.

8 2.2 km

New Forest

9 6.5 km

10 3 km

Page 25

1 **a–c** See cross-section below.

d south-west

e shape of the hills, small valley floor

2 See cross-section below.

Page 28
Looe

1 The woodland is found along the river valleys such as the West Looe river. There is no woodland on the hilltops. There is no woodland above 130 m. There are some small patches of woodland, for example at 2458.

2 The railway line follows the main river valley on the map, the East Looe River. The A387 follows this river for about 3 km, then takes the route around the top of a hill to the east. Other routes mainly follow the river valleys or pass between the hills.

Swanage

3 The main settlement, Swanage, is on the coast. It is between the ranges of hills, one to the north and one to the south. There are small settlements on the slopes of the southern hills such as Worth Matravers (9777). The other larger settlements in the area are Corfe Castle, which has grown close to a gap in the northern hills that allows access to the area. There is also Harman's Cross, which is in the valley halfway between the other two settlements.

4 Straight boundaries and roadways can be seen through the woodland, which allows management. Local knowledge or map evidence provides screen for the oil field to the north.

5 There are roads on either side of the steep hill. The main A351 goes through the main valley. There are few roads to the south of the map and instead steep hills and lack of settlement.

6 a The 1:25 000 shows the most detail, less of the area is shown on the map because of the detail it contains. The 1:50 000 shows the largest area but has the least detail of that area.

b 1:50 000 ferry routes
1:25 000 leisure symbols

c It would depend on what the trip was trying to achieve. If going on a coastal walk the 1:25 000 would be best. If looking at the area they are visiting, the 1:50 000 would be best.

d There are many different answers. Possible ones are below:

1:50 000	1:25 000
Planning a field trip to an area	Going for a walk
Driving in an area	Doing beach surveys

New Forest

7 spit

8 Expect use of key to identify features such as – sandy beach, marshland, shingle, lowland.

9 1491 is very man-made – groynes on beach, built-up area, some cliffs. 1690 is very open and rural, nature trail, low lying.

10 meander bend

11 It is a meander bend, river approximately 75 m wide, built up within 0.5 km of river, the rest is left as floodplain although built-up area closer in some places.

Page 29

1 Geographical Information System

2 Layering is the ability that GIS gives you to put different types of information on a map by overlaying on a computer.

3 ambulance service, supermarket chains, public utility companies, police

4 A satellite navigation system is GIS; this would be used by the delivery person to find your address.

5 land for sale, population density, socio-economic groupings of residents, transport routes, competitors

Comments such as: The land has to be first because otherwise they cannot build the store. The others could be in a different order but if no one lives there then there is no point in putting a shop there.

Page 30

1 Post Office, public house, place of worship with a spire, milestone, road

2

Key:
- A roads
- B roads
- 50 metre contour line
- 100 metre contour line
- East Looe River
- Railway line and station
- Settlement of Looe

Scale: 0   1   2 km

3

Place	Feature on map
Island A	St George's or Looe
Spot height B	115 m
Tourist attraction C	Caravan and camping site
Tourist attraction D	Parking
Road number E	B3254
Road number F	B3253
Settlement G	Port Looe
Type of woodland H	Non-coniferous
Farm I	Puffiland Farm

Page 33

1

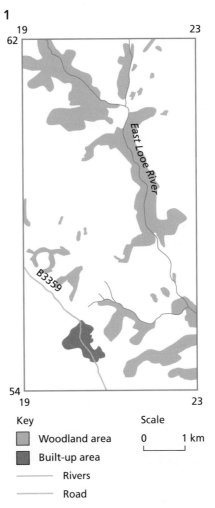

Key
- Woodland area
- Built-up area
- Rivers
- Road

Scale
0   1 km

2 Answer should be a simple sketch with the following marked:
  a the built-up areas of Alnmouth and Warkworth
  b the Rivers Aln and Coquet
  c the coastline and all coastal features
  d any tourist information features in the area

Page 34

Answers such as: The dark colour across the centre of the photo in a bendy line indicates water. The Isle of Dogs meander bend can be seen clearly on the satellite image.

Page 38

1

Ground photo	Oblique aerial photograph	Vertical aerial photograph	Satellite photograph
Shows a small area in detail.	Shows a larger area but less defined.	Shows a smaller area but more detail.	Shows a large area of the coastline.
Can clearly see beach and type of vegetation.	Shows outline of coastline, hills and lowland areas.	Does not show whether the area is flat or hilly. Coastline shown clearly.	Can distinguish beaches and landforms to some extent.
Shows groynes on the beach and houses in the distance.	Shows position of settlements, wooded areas and fields.	Shows areas that are fields and areas that are built up. Shows actual houses, roads/street patterns.	Can identify built-up areas, field patterns and wooded areas.

2 Human features: castle, defensive site, village in the centre of the meander bend, large fields around the village. Physical features: flat land, no sign of animals so probably arable (crop-farming), wide bend (meander) of the river, coastline with sandy beach in the background, which is possibly used by tourists in the summer.

Page 40

1 north-west

2

Letter on photograph	Grid reference	Feature
V	Six figure = 254535	Number of road = A387
W	Four figure = 2454	Name of woodland = Trenant wood
X	Six figure = 257530	Identify symbol = Beacon
Y	Four figure = 2554	Name of river = East Looe River
Z	Six figure = 251537	Identify symbol = Parking

3 Many answers are possible: cars parked, the actual buildings, wooded areas around housing to west of river that are not on the map.

4 Many answers are possible: museum, road numbers, names of villages.

Page 43

1

2

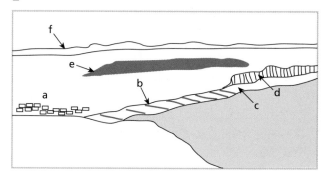

Chapter 3 answers, pages 45–72

Answers to activities

Page 50

1 population pyramid accurately drawn

2 There are large numbers of people in the 20–29 age group: 15 per cent males and 12 per cent females. There are very few people over the age of 69: only 13.5 per cent.

3 – It clearly shows whether any of the age groups has more of the population than the others.
– The data is continuous.

4 All of the countries have a winter maximum. The amount that they have in summer is very low, the highest being 80 mm in Rome. The lowest summer total is in Tripoli with 1 mm. The highest winter total is Tel Aviv, the lowest is 125 mm in Tripoli. Tel Aviv has the greatest difference between summer and winter precipitation, Rome the smallest.

Page 56

1 Advantages: shows at a glance the peaks and flows in the traffic, comparisons between times are easy to make, easy to construct, continuous data. Disadvantages: can be a problem if the number of vehicles varies greatly between the times, would be better if displayed as a flow line map because it doesn't show direction, which a flow line map would.

2 a flow line map
   b It shows direction as well as numbers of vehicles.
   c Many more people went into Lulworth on Sunday than any other flow. The peak flow was 136 vehicles between 2 p.m. and 2.30 p.m. The lowest flow is out of Lulworth on Friday p.m. between 3 p.m. and 3.30 p.m., when ten vehicles left Lulworth.

3 Arrows should go along the streets where the people walked. There is no scale on the key. The arrows are different lengths. It is not clear from the location of the arrows where the counts were actually completed. The number of pedestrians should not be written on the arrows, it should be determined from the key.

4 map redrawn taking the points in question 3 into consideration

5 histogram

6 compound line graph drawn as in the 'how to' box on page 53

Page 57

1 pie diagram as in Figure 11

2 The number employed in primary industry has declined from about 8 per cent in 1991 to about 2 per cent in 2006. The number in secondary industry declined between 1991 and 2001. It was then fairly stable between 2001 and 2006. Tertiary industry has increased over the whole period from about 63 per cent in 1991 to 85 per cent in 2006.

3 compound bar chart

Page 59

1 The pictogram could be pictures of people but better if pictures are of different vehicles.

2 bar chart

3 Pictures of vehicles show clearly what has been counted. Numbers of vehicles can be seen easily by the key.

4 Data is more accurately presented. The chart is much easier to construct.

Page 61

1 choropleth drawn

2 Most tourists go to France with 81.9 million tourists visiting there. The tenth most popular world tourist destination is Mexico with 21.4 million tourists. (This is the least to expect. There should be other comments about countries within these figures.)

3 Advantages: shows immediately at a glance the pattern made by the data, visual representation is easy to complete.
Disadvantages: only shows a spread of data not an amount, the ranges of data used can make the map ineffective in showing the pattern.

4 bars on a map of the world

5 The bars immediately show the amount by their height with a choropleth the key would need to be referred to. The choropleth does not show a specific amount but a range of data.

6 A histogram is better for continuous data.

Page 63

1 map completed

2 The greatest number of tourists went to Spain with 14 million visitors. The least number of tourists went to Portugal, Greece, the Netherlands and Turkey with only 2 million. The only destination in the top ten that is not in Europe is the USA with 4 million tourist visits.

3 Advantages: shows clearly the differences due to the different sizes of the circles; shows location so the spread of the data can be seen at a glance. Disadvantages: difficult to construct; data is shown in a range not an actual value.

Page 65

1 scatter graph drawn

2 There is a positive correlation.

3 New Zealand, Algeria

4 If a country has piped water to houses, more water will be used. It is a percentage therefore that will alternate with the other uses, which are agriculture and industry. If the country is a dry one, the agricultural percentage will be higher.

Page 67

1 dispersion graph completed

2 Pebbles are larger at site 1. The largest pebble at site 2 is still as large as the middle range of pebbles at site 1. The smallest pebble is 3 mm at site 2 but site 1 has a pebble only 2 mm bigger. Therefore, there is little difference between the sizes.

3   The pattern shown is that the smaller pebbles are found at the second site. The larger pebbles are found at the source of the river.
4   scatter graph
5   It would also show the dispersion of the pebbles.
6   The dots on the graph could have been a certain shape. Therefore, they could have drawn a pictogram of the shape of the pebble on the graph where the size was located.

Page 69

1   Radial diagram drawn
2   The greatest number of tourists went to Spain with 14 million visitors. The least number of tourists went to the Netherlands and Turkey with 2 million. The only destination in the top ten not in Europe is the USA with 4 million tourists.
3   The diagram shows the direction as well as the number of tourists.
4   A histogram would show the countries and numbers of tourists.
5   The techniques will both show the data clearly but the rose diagram will also show the direction of the destinations from the UK. The length of the lines showing the number of tourists would be more effective than drawing bars.

Page 71

1   Triangular graph constructed
2   The country with the highest number of people employed in the primary sector is Ethiopia with 84 per cent. The country with the lowest number employed in the primary sector is the UK with 2 per cent. The country that is spread most evenly between the sectors is Mexico. The country with the largest number employed in secondary is Japan.
3   Advantages: They are able to show three sets of data on one graph. It is very easy to see the patterns they portray. Anomalies are easy to spot. They can save a lot of time and effort because a lot of information is on one graph.
Disadvantages: They are difficult to construct. They can be confusing if you are unsure which way to read the lines. They have to be conducted for data that adds up to 100 per cent.
4   Nine

Page 72

1   Kite diagram drawn
2   The amount of sea couch grass decreases with movement away from the coast. The percentage cover of birch trees increases with distance from the coast. Other vegetation varies, for instance marram grass is dominant at 150 metres from the coast.
3   Advantages: – Visual representation with distance, very easy to read the data and understand. Limitations: Subjective on how to set out the diagram. Difficult to draw accurately.

Chapter 4 answers, pages 73–90

Answers to activities

Page 79

1   Hypotheses such as:
The barrage would have a detrimental effect on fish stocks in the area.
The barrage would have a negative visual impact on the area.
2   Devise techniques to test for the presence of longshore drift, carry out the fieldwork, collate results, present the data, analyse, conclude and evaluate your work.
3   a Hypotheses/questions such as:
The width of the river will increase as it flows from source to mouth.
The velocity of the river will increase as it flows from source to mouth.
See sequence of enquiry on page 75.
    b These will be individual to the student but should include location of survey(s), room to write down a number of techniques at each site, and space for repetition of sampling.
    c Again, individual responses but must include explanation.
4   Answers will vary depending upon technique chosen.

Page 90

1   student's own answer
2   a Analyse means to describe and explain. For example, Sunday was a busier day than Friday with a total of 327 vehicles going into Lulworth whereas on Friday only 169 vehicles went into Lulworth, a difference of 158 vehicles. This may be because Sunday is the weekend and fewer people are at work or school.
    b Conclusions may be that Lulworth is much busier at the weekend than in the week because many more vehicles came and left the car park.

Chapter 5 answers, pages 91–105

Answers to exam-style questions

Page 92

Warkworth map

1 a south
   b iv River Coquet   (2 marks)
2 2611 flat rock
   2507 beach
   2605 dunes   (3 marks)
3 See sketch map for answers.   (5 marks)

4 The river valley is at a height of 10 m. The river is in its lower course near the sea. The river has many (meander) bends. A railway line crosses the river in grid square 2212. In grid square 2311, the river is crossed by the A1068. The river flows to the south of Lesbury. There is a small coniferous woodland to the south of the river in grid square 2211. (4 marks)

5 Leave Hermitage Farm, turn left onto the secondary road. After approximately 1 km, arrive at a junction with the A1068. Turn left onto the A1068 towards Alnmouth, drive for approximately 5 km. Go straight across the roundabout in grid square 2311, continuing on the A1068. After approximately 5 km, you will then reach the town of Alnwick. Continue through the town on the B6341, parking in the car park close to the castle. (4 marks)

Page 94

Wensleydale map

1 a i River Ure   (1 mark)
   b iii west to east   (1 mark)

2

Service	Hawes	Bainbridge
Public house	✓	✓
Place of worship with a spire	✓	
Visitor centre	✓	
Post Office	✓	

(4 marks)

3 Any three tourist features from the map key: visitor centre, craft centre, and so on. (3 marks)
4 9182   (1 mark)
5 230 m 535 m = 305 m   (1 mark)
6 The settlements are in the valleys because that is where the main road is (the A684). The settlements are not on the hills because they are too steep. This is shown by the contour lines being close together. The settlements are found in the river valleys to have easy access to water for drinking. (4 marks)
7 The River Ure bends. It has a wide flat valley floor about 0.5 km. The river flows from west to east. There is a caravan site to the south of the river. It is approximately 220 m above sea level. Cragdale water has a number of smaller bends than the Ure, which has one big one in the section we are looking at. It has steep sides and very little flat land in the valley bottom. The river flows from south-east to north-west. (5 marks)

Page 94

New Forest map

1 west   (1 mark)
2 beach 1391, parking 1691, nature trail 1690/1691, nature reserve 1790, PC 1691 (3 marks)
3 meander bend, floodplain, levee (1 mark)
4 river estuary, headland, spit, mud and sand, marshland   (3 marks)
5 There is a headland with a spit which has been formed due to Longshore drift occurring along the coastline. (1 mark)

Pages 97–98

Looe map

1   S = St. George's or Looe Island
     T = Flat rock   (2 marks)
2   It is a wet point site. It has a spring in the
     village, which would have supplied water to the
     villagers. It is above the floodplain of the river. It
     is on the junction of a number of secondary roads.
                                                        (4 marks)
3   one mark for each label and one mark for drawing
     the cross-section

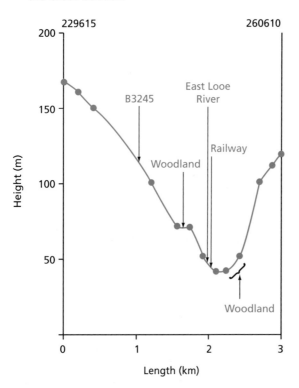

                                                        (5 marks)

4   a   museum, IRB station, information centre, place
         of worship with a tower   (3 marks)
     b   boats, benches, promenade   (1 mark)

Page 101

Cambridge map

1   a   4657   (1 mark)
     b   railway station   (1 mark)
     c   472572   (1 mark)
     d   A1134   (1 mark)

e   The housing is in a grid-iron pattern. This means
     that the housing is in blocks. The streets are in a
     line and meet each other at right angles. (3 marks)

2   a   cul-de-sacs, curves, not in a straight line
         compared to comments in 1e
         (comparative comment not required,
         implicit comparison is satisfactory)   (3 marks)
     b   The housing is on cheaper land at the
         edge of the city.   (1 mark)
3

	On map not on photograph	On photograph not on map
Feature 1	Churches	Fields
Feature 2	Road numbers	Types of buildings

                                                        (2 marks)

4   The 'park and ride' sites are all on the outskirts of
     Cambridge. They are close to major roads that
     lead into the city. There is a 'park and ride' site
     in grid square 4259. This is close to a motorway
     junction.   (3 marks)

Page 105

Swanage map

1   a   B3351   (1 mark)
     b   035822   (1 mark)
     c   National Trust   (1 mark)
     d   Camp and caravan site   (1 mark)
     e   5   (1 mark)
2   Harman's Cross is a linear village. Most of the
     houses are either side of the main A351 road.
     The village of Worth Matravers has a more
     nucleated shape with the houses being grouped
     around a junction.   (3 marks)
3   Sketch (1 mark), accurately shading the town
     of Swanage (1 mark), beach and groynes (1 mark)
     and Swanage Bay (1 mark), Peveril Point (1 mark),
     the pier (1 mark).   (6 marks)

Index